THE CHAKRAS
ACTIVITY BOOK & JOURNAL

GET GROUNDED, FEEL GOOD, FREE YOUR CHI
& LOTS OF OTHER COOL MAGICAL STUFF

KNOCK KNOCK®
LOS ANGELES, CALIFORNIA

GREETINGS, CHAKRA-NAUTS!

Whether you're a brand-new, bright-eyed, freshly hatched chakra baby, gingerly tiptoeing into the world of energetic healing for the first time or a wise and ancient soul who's been talking chakra shop for millennia, waiting for the rest of the world to catch on, fingers crossed you'll get some genuine glow from this collection of meditations, games, and activities aimed at nurturing your chakras and bringing greater peace and fulfillment to your life. (Or, at the very least, some well-intentioned procrastination to divert you from more pressing, boring tasks.)

You don't have to read straight through this book from start to finish, though when working with chakras it's recommended you go in order (because positive flow of energy and all that). So feel free to choose a random activity or two from each section, then go back and do the same thing the next time you're in need of an existential "tune-up." And don't worry about those unfinished activities—chakra healing can work wonders on the ol' OCD. The great news is, there's no wrong way to improve yourself. (Um. We'll debate face tattoos later.) No amount of loving awareness is ever wasted, so do what feels right to you, have fun, and be well!

**ALL SYSTEMS GO!
LIFE IS GREAT!
I DON'T EVEN NEED THIS BOOK!**

**UH-OH.
IT'S ONLY TUESDAY???????
WHY DID I JUST CRY IN
A PANDA EXPRESS?**

CHAKRAS: A TEENY-TINY HISTORY

The word *chakra* (ancient Sanskrit for "wheel of light" or modern English for "there's a good chance I live on the West Coast") first appeared in Hindu texts around 3,000 years ago. Since then, the wisdom of chakra healing has humbly made its way into half a dozen religions, philosophies, and other "isms," as well as both Eastern and Western medicine. Acupuncturists and Jungian psychologists alike are privy to the power of chakras, and yoga teachers, of course, are grateful for all the topical patter. But what in the world are chakras, and why do you only hear about them when yours are out of alignment— or when you're in the crystal jewelry section of the local craft fair?

ALL ABOUT ENERGY

We've all got physical bodies (unless you're a ghost reading this over someone's shoulder, in which case welcome, and no discrimination intended)—and we've got energetic bodies too. Our energetic bodies are fields of electromagnetic energy that surround and permeate us, and can be seen as a sort of a stepping stone between the physical world and the etheric one (AKA the realm where energy, radio waves, and other "unseens" hang out together). In certain spots, our physical and energetic bodies are connected to each other via spiraling energy centers known as chakras. These are sort of like etheric umbilical cords that channel vast amounts of energy into and out of our physical bodies. Bet some of you already knew that (shout-out to our ghost friends).

A main player in this energy flow is something called subtle energy, known by one of several dozen aliases depending on your culture and tradition*. Subtle energy vibrates at a higher frequency than solid matter. It's affected by light and sound, and is much more malleable than, say, human anatomy. Like a magnetic field pulling on a paperclip, it impacts our physical world, and can offer a bit of shortcut in healing stress, illness, or other physical deficits.

Ways to move, heal, or say "hey there!" to your energy range from fringe to mainstream—you may have seen, tried, fantasized about trying, or curiously google-stalked some of them yourself. Most likely to ring a bell: acupuncture, tai chi, reiki, reflexology, light/color/aromatherapy, sound baths, crystal healing, and yoga.

Working with chakras is sort of like working on our subtle energy subway system; if we can keep our main energetic ports operating as planned, then subtle energy can move through us freely and not get stuck on a crowded train for no reason when it has a bunch of stuff to do and no way of calling its friends because there's no phone signal down there. Y'know?

*chi, qi, prana, mana, spirit, consciousness, life force, and "Steven" to name a few.

MEET YOUR CHAKRAS

There are seven chakras (well, seven major ones that is—but those are the ones we'll stick with to keep this simplification, um…simple) arranged like beads along our spinal column. When they're aligned, clear, and functioning properly, they create a perfect energetic channel that runs from the top of your head down to your tailbone. Your inner poet might say there's a shimmering beam of light streaming down from the stars into your body, and another energetic beam blasting up from the core of the planet to meet it. Sounds like a pretty decent happy hour!

If you prefer hard science, well, take note that the seven major chakras correspond with the seven most significant glands in our endocrine system (AKA the captains of "Team Hormone"). When the system is functioning at full tilt, we're happy, healthy, and able to leap over difficult moments in a single bound. When it's out of whack, we become any number of not-ideal versions of ourselves, from "rage monster" to "relentlessly-needy-and-obsessively-insecure-even-though-our-partner-has-shown-a-totally-normal-amount-of-affection monster." Fun!

Each chakra corresponds with a color, and (thankfully for us) those colors create a totally eye-pleasing rainbow spectrum. In ascending order, from 1 (the root chakra) to 7 (the crown), they govern emotions and issues of increasing consciousness. In other words, the lower chakras deal with our base human needs and petty earthly concerns, and our highest chakras connect us to a universal oneness that fosters unconditional love for all beings everywhere. If you're into that sort of thing.

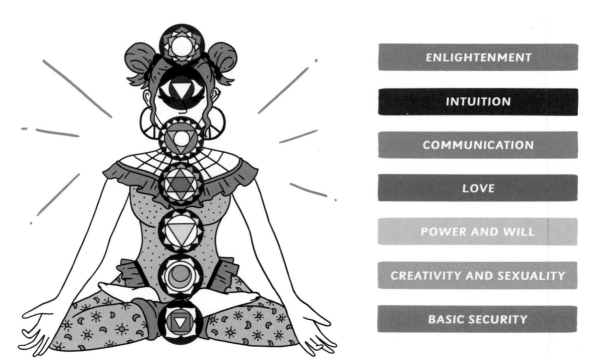

ENLIGHTENMENT

INTUITION

COMMUNICATION

LOVE

POWER AND WILL

CREATIVITY AND SEXUALITY

BASIC SECURITY

GETTING TO WORK

When a chakra is imbalanced, overactive, closed, blocked, stagnant, or any other trait you'd never want to put on a dating profile, you'll likely see evidence of it—both in the form of physical/mental/emotional symptoms, and as annoyingly on-the-nose echoes of the blockage in your daily life. For example, a compromised root chakra might cause sleeplessness and anxiety about money…followed by (and here's the kicker) actual financial scarcity. This of course will only feed said anxiety-snake with its proverbial "I told you so!" tail, and continue the cycle of insecurity, which isn't fun for anyone (least of all that poor self-cannibalizing snake).

The good news is, none of this is permanent! It's true that chakras are sensitive to life's dramas, and they can even hold the resonance of past traumas, but thankfully they are dynamic energy centers and not chiseled stone (which would have made for a horrendous design flaw). With a little bit of mindful attention and some sensory TLC, you can realign your chakras and get them back to being open, clear, clean, smart, talented, kind, easy to talk to, good at board games…you get the idea.

There are dozens of ways to work on opening and balancing chakras, and you'll learn about a bunch of 'em in this book. Take color, for example. Each chakra corresponds to a specific color, and one simple way to work with that chakra is to look at, meditate on, or wear that shade. Feeling broken-hearted? Throw on your best green sweat suit and do your crying under a green light bulb. Light and color therapists say you'll be feeling better in no time. (They, of course, are not the ones dealing with the nasty breakup.) You'll also notice that each chakra resonates with certain foods (eat them!), essential oils (smell them!), songs (listen to them!), and stones (hold them, carry them, or bathe with them!). Yoga is very helpful for moving energy in general—but certain yoga poses are aces for unblocking energetic traffic jams in each chakra. You'll find a handy list of all of this at the top of each chakra chapter.

But enough about the basics—are you ready to be the reigning master of your own subtle energetic destiny? Good answer! Here we go!

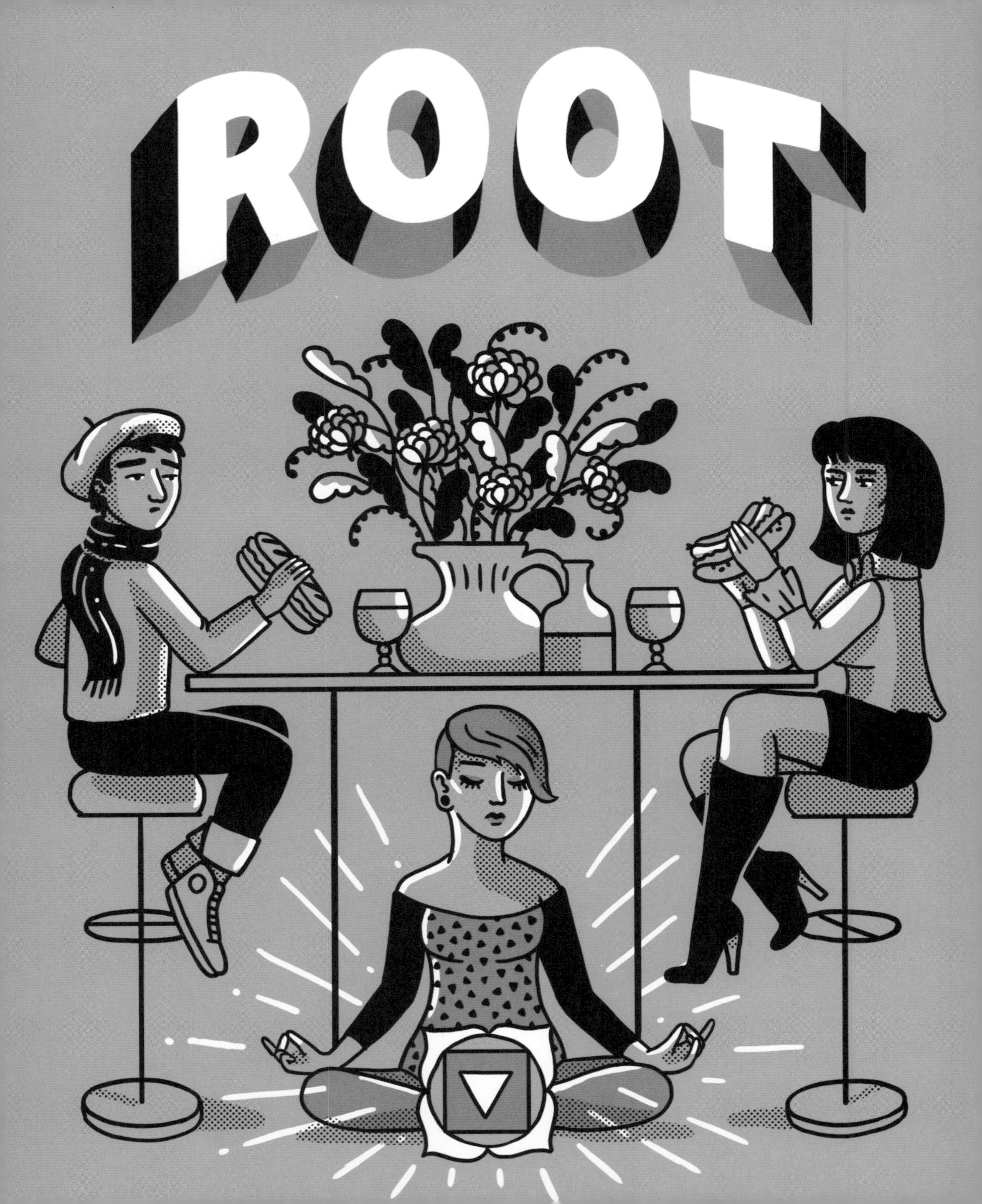
ROOT

MULADHARA (ROOT) CHAKRA

The root chakra keeps you anchored to the physical world, and acts like, yep, a root. Like the roots on a tree, it makes for an in-with-the-good/out-with-the-bad setup that's basically an ethereal recycling center. You get fed a never-ending buffet of all the planetary energy you need, and you simultaneously get to unload your chaotic human static back into Mama Earth's loving arms. This, of course, is the only situation in which dumping our garbage into the planet is totally acceptable.

When you think of the root chakra, picture your inner cave-person. Your root craves connection to the planet, and also connection to (and celebration of) your physical senses…the feel of sand between your toes; the smell of salt in the air; the taste of—what is that?—ceviche? It wants you to live in your body, and it wants that body to remember that it lives on the earth. Think Tarzan. Think barefoot dancers. Think anyone who's currently taking a pottery class.

WHEN YOUR ROOT'S RIGHT:
You feel safe, secure, and trusting. Life may throw some curve balls, but you swing at them with an unconditionally good attitude. Unexpected parking ticket? You'll shrug it off.

"You know what? I'm lucky I haven't gotten more."

WHEN YOUR ROOT'S BLOCKED:
Depression and anxiety rule the day. You spend sleepless nights worrying about money, health, and other basics, and disturbing days feeling like you can't get your act together.

"What's wrong with me? How am I supposed to exist? I need pasta."

WHEN YOUR ROOT'S OVERACTIVE:
Anxiety spins into paranoia, greed, and control. This is the realm of hoarding and eating disorders.

"I have to save these old Sears catalogues. What if I need them some day and don't have them? THEN WHAT??"

KEY CONCEPTS:

* Safety
* Security
* Physicality
* Abundance
* Basic Human Needs*

LOCATION:
Between the Anus and Genitals

TO OPEN AND BALANCE YOUR ROOT:
Color: Red
Essential Oils: Cedarwood, Myrrh, Patchouli
Stones:

* Overactive = Emerald, Sapphire
* Blocked = Red Jasper, Hematite
* For General Balance = Red Carnelian

Yoga Poses: Warrior 1, Triangle, Forward Bend
Musical Key: C
Foods: Beets, Red Berries, Radishes, Peppers, Kidney Beans, Root Vegetables

ROOT CHAKRA PLAYLIST (SONGS IN THE KEY OF C):

"Halo" (Beyoncé)
"Let It Be" (The Beatles)
"I Will Survive" (Gloria Gaynor)
"Hallelujah" (Jeff Buckley)
"No Woman No Cry" (Bob Marley)
"Ain't No Mountain" (Diana Ross)
"Private Eyes" (Hall & Oates)
"Killing Me Softly" (Fugees)

* No offense, needs. But you are very, very basic.

THE CHAKRA DOCT-RA IS IN!

Take the temp of your root by coloring in one segment on the thermometer for each symptom you're displaying. The higher the temp, the more your root needs pampering. Homemade root noodle soup? (Results are completely accurate, utterly scientific, and therefore totally irrefutable.*)

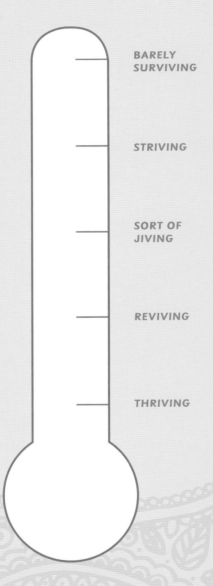

BARELY SURVIVING

STRIVING

SORT OF JIVING

REVIVING

THRIVING

* Depressed (Even more than usual, with even less reason. Although these days, do we need a reason?)

* Restless, sleepless, zombie-like (And yet despite the extra waking hours—somehow useless?)

* Lacking focus, fuzzy-brained

* Obsessed with your finances (e.g., constantly checking your bank account/counting spare change/taking stock of every invisible asset from airline miles to coffee shop punch cards)

* Eating like you're pregnant/certain you're not pregnant/wondering if you wouldn't mind being pregnant

* Allergic to change ("WHO THE &#*@ DID THE DISHES THAT WERE IN THE SINK?????")

* Did we already say lacking focus?

* Swollen legs or feet, lower back troubles, definitely not pregnant

* Co-dependence (Ironically hard to self-diagnose. Maybe ask the person you check in with 79,000 times a day?)

* Resentful of friends; defensive with strangers; quick to anger (In other words, an all-around peach.)

* Lacking focu...s

*Because we said so.

ROOT CHAKRA BINGO!

Complete five in a row and your root will be in tip-top (tip-bottom?) shape.

Do one hour of yoga. (Even better if it's by candlelight.)	Eat some STEW. (Bonus points for cooking it yourself!)	Bathe with garnet, carnelian, hematite, or bloodstone. (The water helps carry the resonance of the crystal!)	Meditate with your butt scooched up against the base of a tree. (Nudity optional.)	Put your toes in the dirt, walk barefoot on grass, or lie in the sand.
Dance barefoot for at least 15 minutes. (Or significantly longer if you're really feelin' it.)	Sit in lotus pose and breathe deeply. On every exhalation, say "Uhhhhhhh."	Make something—anything!—out of clay. (Extra credit if it's actually useful to someone.)	Make a fire. Sit by that fire. Stare for a long time at that fire. Let the flames burn away all of your negative thoughts.	Spend some QT with the scent of cedarwood or myrrh essential oils.
Finger paint. The messier the better.	Sit quietly and listen to the sound of rain. (Recordings are OK if it's sunny out.)	Roll around in the grass.	Do five forward bends. Breathe deeply into each one.	Work in a garden. If you can, eat something from that garden. If it's tasty, say "Mmm."
Plant something green.	Wear red head-to-toe for a day. (Red undies count double!)	Repeat the mantra: "I am that I am" over the course of a whole day whenever you think of it.	Drink beet juice and/or roast some beets and other root veggies.	Play drums. Or, if feasible, attend a drum circle, man.
Listen to Mongolian throat singing.	Make a list of people you're grateful for. Write some "just cuz" thank you notes to those people. Continue your gratitude.	Spend 20 minutes visualizing vibrant red light connecting your root to the center of the earth.	Stand barefoot in a river or stream. Make friends twith at least three stones you find pretty.	Spend a night outside under the stars—either in a tent or in the open air.

TREE-FOR-ALL

Ever taken a "forest bath" (or as they call it in Japan, *shinrin-yoku*)? It helps to lower stress, improve relationships, increase focus, and heal from illness. Here's how: stand in—or walk slowly through—a forest, breathe in the energy from the trees, and give your worries to the roots. They gotchu.

WHAT'S FEEDING YOU?

Color the rings of the tree trunk with the corresponding shades, and get a good look at what you're taking in. Is there anything you'd like to be nourished by that you're not getting enough of? Vitamin "me"?

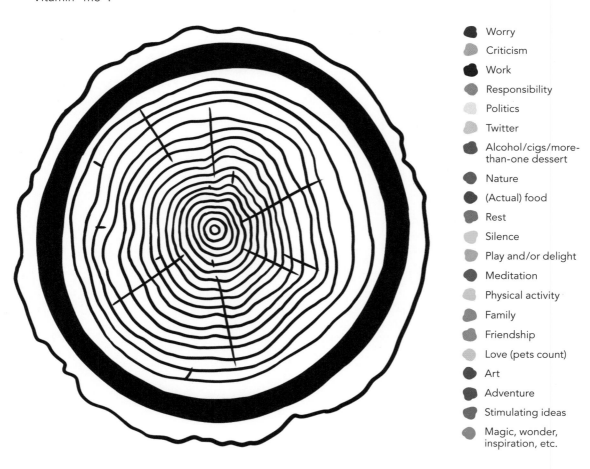

- Worry
- Criticism
- Work
- Responsibility
- Politics
- Twitter
- Alcohol/cigs/more-than-one dessert
- Nature
- (Actual) food
- Rest
- Silence
- Play and/or delight
- Meditation
- Physical activity
- Family
- Friendship
- Love (pets count)
- Art
- Adventure
- Stimulating ideas
- Magic, wonder, inspiration, etc.

DEAR ME!

Write a letter to yourself when you were a kid. Pick a specific age—the one that feels like you most needed a hug or a double high five. Tell this littler you all the reasons you're awesome, say why you're proud of you, maybe draw yourself a trophy. Tell you some of the wonderful, amazing things you're going to love about your life. Then, take a moment to recognize that you're actually living that wonderful, amazing life right now.

VACATION / STAYCATION / DOESN'T HAVE TO BE OUT OF THE WAY-CATION

My favorite place to retreat/recharge/regroup until I'm a fully functioning human again:

_____

_____

But if I can't make it there anytime soon, here's an easier-to-get-to place that evokes a lot of the same regroup-y vibes:

_____

_____

And in case I can't get away at all, here are some things I love about my aforementioned "there" that I don't get a lot of "here":

_____

_____

And here are things I can do to consciously sprinkle a little more "there" in my "here":

_____

_____

_____

Regardless of where I am, I promise to give myself some type of retreat. If I can go to my A place, great. If not, the B team will do. And if that can't happen, I vow to make the most of plan C, and really truly give myself that recharge (even if it's just with a two dollar candle and a library book).

My signature, making this a legally-binding agreement with myself:

Name: _____

Date: _____

HOME SWEET (BUT IT CAN BE SWEETER) HOME

Your root chakra loves to root itself in security, comfort, and all things inviting-and-cozy. Use this page to outline and execute a plan for cleaning, cozy-ing, or otherwise improving your living space. Remember—it doesn't cost money to make a nest you're proud of. If birds can pull it off, so can we!

Some tiny, totally affordable changes that would easily and instantly improve my living space are:

_____   _____

_____   _____

_____   _____

_____   _____

Some larger changes I can plan/save for, and make in the next few months or so are:

_____   _____

_____   _____

_____   _____

_____   _____

Finally, my signed promise that I will do a balls-out deep-clean this week: _____

ABUNDANCE ABOUNDS!

Even when our wallets are making us feel cash poor, we've always got plenty of riches in our lives.

On each coin, write the name of something you're lucky to have in your life. (Pro tip: Specificity will get you more bang for your buck.)

Name as many things as you can! Love, friendship, warm socks, travel mugs, your fake-but-realistic potted ficus, that airbrushed dragon hoodie you scored at the middle-school rummage sale…no spark of joy is too small to be left out of your tally of riches.

ABUNDANCE BY THE NUMBERS

When aiming your arrows toward abundant thinking, it's helpful to remember that abundance isn't scarce. It is, in fact, abundant. Use the numbers on the right to answer the trivia on the left…and remind your root that abundance is the happy tendency of the entire universe.

* Number of plant species on Earth
* Average number of minutes spent commuting each day in L.A.
* Number of cells in a human body
* Number of calories in a Thanksgiving dinner
* Number of acting credits Meryl Streep has on IMDB
* Number of unique insect species on earth
* Average number of seeds in a strawberry
* Average matches on Tinder per day
* Longest recorded stretch of consecutive rainy/snowy days in one place
* Average number of times you fart each year

* 391,000	* 54
* 15 million	* 4,500
* 5,110	* 88
* 83	* 37.2 trillion
* 10 quintillion (10,000,000,000,000,000,000)	* 200

Answers
Plant Species = 391,000; Commuting in LA = 54; Cells = 37.2 trillion; Calories = 4,500; Acting Credits = 83; Insect Species = 10 quintillion (10,000,000,000,000,000,000); Strawberry = 200; Tinder = 15 million; Rainy/snowy days = 88; Farts = 5110

GET (UN)TANGLED

Zentangle is a meditative art practice that's all about drawing simple repeated patterns to fill a space (no drawing ability necessary, which is probably what makes it so darn meditative). Practice your new-found (totally innate) zentangle talents below and lose yourself in this very root-worthy mantra.

HERE'S HOW:

1. Choose a zentangle pattern below—or create your own!
2. Decorate the first letter with that pattern, repeating until all are filled in.
3. If you'd like to really go to town, feel free to color it in too!
4. Move on to the next letter and do it all over again, this time with a different pattern.
5. Keep on truckin' till your zentangle masterpiece is complete.
6. Take a sec to admire your work, then give your fingers a little shout-out for creating something cool.

YOU'RE GROUNDED!

Can you find these grounding words hidden in the roots?

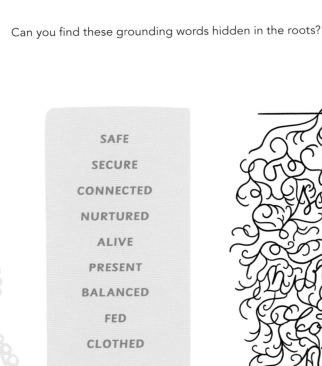

SAFE

SECURE

CONNECTED

NURTURED

ALIVE

PRESENT

BALANCED

FED

CLOTHED

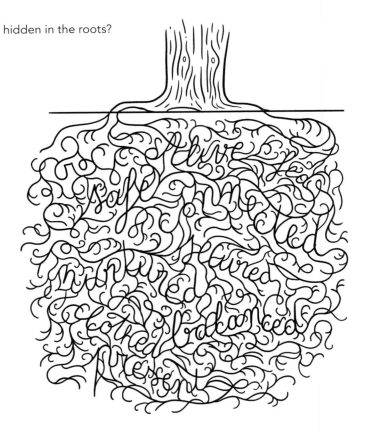

PERSPECTIVE TUNE-UP

Have you been accidentally wearing a prescription for not-so-rosy-colored glasses? See if you can upgrade your outlook with a quick round-the-room scavenger hunt.

TRY SPOTTING:

* Something that makes your life sorta-better-than-average
* Something that excited you (at least at once)
* Something that gives you a little challenge
* Something that keeps you warm
* Something that keeps you going
* Something that keeps your stress in check

* Something that reminds you where you came from (for better or worse)
* Something that confirms you're human
* Something that was given to you "just because"
* Something you could probably live without (but would rather not)

"I AM" COLLAGE

What makes you the most "you" of all? What puts the most you-ness in your "you"? Scour your favorite magazines, websites, or even old pics (no judgment!) and glue/tape/staple them here to create a visual feast of all the things that ring your "I am" bell.

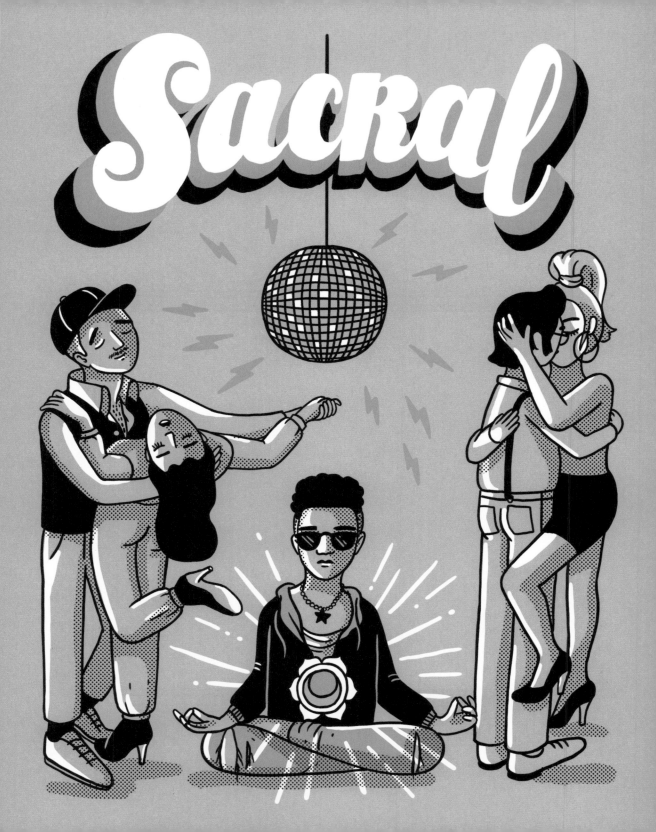

SVADHISHTHANA (SACRAL) CHAKRA

The sacral chakra is the first step up in our ladder of consciousness. After our root chakra has taken our only-visible-to-people-who-see-auras energy and channeled it into the cold, hard reality shock of a physical body—and after that body is fed/clothed/certain that it's not inside of a tiger's mouth, we are free begin to explore the next realm: pleasure, relationships, and creativity.

The sacral chakra is sort of like the spark that ignites all our inner fires. It's the bolt from the blue that makes us want to sit down and write/draw/paint/learn the trombone. It's the impulse behind the desire to, um, "connect" with someone. It's the flicker of passion that flies through our hearts when we taste a delicious food or dance to an amazing song or read an exciting book about vampires who attend high school.

WHEN YOUR SACRAL'S RIGHT:
Intimacy will be easy, relationships will be healthy, and inspiration will flow freely.

"Take that, Sunday! Pass the rosé."

WHEN YOUR SACRAL'S BLOCKED:
You'll slog through low libido, a fear of intimacy, shame, creative self-sabotage, and/or a general, all-encompassing lack of enthusiasm.

"You ever read that story where Tigger loses his bounce?"

WHEN YOUR SACRAL'S OVERACTIVE:
Get ready for bursts of untamed emotion ("USE YOUR TURN SIGNAL, YA JAG!!!!"), unhealthy relationships ("I looked at your phone again. Who the hell is Mom ICE?"), and/or off-the-charts indulgence.

"You know what goes great with round-the-clock sex? Cocaine."

KEY CONCEPTS:
* Pleasure
* Creativity
* Sexuality
* Needs
* Emotions
* Passion
* Inspiration

LOCATION:
A Few Inches Below the Navel

TO OPEN AND BALANCE YOUR SACRAL:
Color: Orange
Essential Oils: Sandalwood, Ylang-Ylang, Jasmine
Stones:
* Overactive = Emerald
* Blocked = Carnelian
* For General Balance = Moonstone

Yoga Pose: Twisting Triangle
Musical Key: D
Food: Sweet Potatoes, Salmon, Carrots, Apricots, Peaches, Oranges

SACRAL CHAKRA PLAYLIST (SONGS IN THE KEY OF D):

"Waterloo" (Abba)
"Under Pressure" (Queen)
"Should I Stay or Should I Go" (The Clash)
"Cherish" (Madonna)
"Moves Like Jagger" (Maroon 5)
"Sunshine of Your Love" (Cream)

WHERE DO YOU LINE UP?

RELATIONSHIPS

Never had a fight. Support and unconditional love abound. Could be scripted by Hallmark.

You fight, but fairly. You get over it. You'd never talk shit about each other.

Rage is triggered by merely existing. Insults are more common than actual names.

CREATIVITY

A near constant stream of genius ideas. Frequent bouts of staying up late and writing on mirrors with markers.

Making things feels playful, fun, and low pressure.

The slightest bit of inspiration is immediately chased away by a negative self-talk spiral. Your face frequently has pillow marks on it.

PLEASURE AND PASSION

No feeling of need. A state beyond cravings. Abstaining begets the biggest buzz.

Satisfying, shame-free sex life; healthy relationship with alcohol, tacos, and all other drugs.

Complete inability to delay gratification in any form. Insatiable appetite for sex, danger, and other rebellions against good judgment.

NOT YOUR BEST LOOK / COULD BE ROCK BOTTOM

NOODLE DOODLES!

Time to activate your sacral chakra by firing all your creativity neurons. Use your imagination to envision a completed picture, then add whatever lines you need to in order to turn these meaningless scribbles into all-out masterpieces. (And feel free to rotate the page if you want. Sacral chakra don't care!)

YOU TOTALLY GOT THIS
(WHATEVER "THIS" IS)

To make your own inspirational poster, find a picture in a magazine of something you find tacky, useless, or any other version of "how is this a thing?" and paste it on this page. Cause if that thing's a thing, your thing can totally be a thing too. The only difference is, they already made their thing… so what are you waiting for?

INSPIRATION

If this thing got made…

BURN IT UP TO BURN IT DOWN

Our sacral chakra can carry energetic imprints from our past relationships (AKA baggage). Like rocks that are piled up in the middle of a river, any emotional garbage we allow to hang around ends up slowing and blocking our energetic flow. Cut out the squares below, and unload any toxic baggage you're tired of carrying from relationships past by putting that baggage in writing. Then literally throw the papers into a fire (with passion and intention, but without burning the house down or anything) and watch them go up in flames. Your past grievances will now be nothing but ashes and smoke…and overt symbolism.

Person I have negative feelings about:

The garbage emotions I will no longer hold onto:

Person I have negative feelings about:

The garbage emotions I will no longer hold onto:

Thing I have negative feelings about:

The garbage emotions I will no longer hold onto:

Thing I have negative feelings about:

The garbage emotions I will no longer hold onto:

Situation I have negative feelings about:

The garbage emotions I will no longer hold onto:

Situation I have negative feelings about:

The garbage emotions I will no longer hold onto:

STICKS AND STONES
(AND OTHER OPTIONS!)

The sacral chakra is the mascot of healthy relationships, and it's constantly rooting for our best selves to do the talking (even when we're talking about the worst stuff). Use the words and phrases below to fill in the word bubbles.

In version 1, be the crappiest you that you can imagine. In version 2, be the shining-est shiny example that the crappiest you can look up to. (Not pictured: version 3, the play-at-home version, in which you engage in a real-life dialogue with a loved one, and hopefully remember to choose shiny over crappy.)

* Dumb fart
* A little cranky
* Spend another second with
* Awesome human
* An idiot
* Support
* Pull your damn weight
* Aware of that
* Take a minute (I got this!)
* Insane

VERSION 1:

"You _____.

You should

_____."

"It makes me

_____

when you do that.

"Are you _____?"

"How can I

_____ you?"

VERSION 2:

"You _____.

You should

_____."

"It makes me

_____

when you do that.

"Are you _____?"

"How can I

_____ you?"

HAPPY LITTLE COLORS

Bob Ross, slinger of stress-evaporating sayings, and painter of (probably) billions of "happy little trees" was onto something when he touted the "joy of painting." Like he says, "We artists are a different breed of people. We're a happy bunch."

Your sacral chakra is ignited whenever you harness your inner artist—if only just by grabbing some paint and a brush and mashing colors together. Read the titles of the made-up paint samples below, then fill them with colors of your own creation to get your sacral chakra flowing, and start your career as an imaginary color inventor.

VINTAGE
BRIDESMAID

PUPPY PAW

CIRCUS
PEANUT

FUN MOM

SOUP OF
THE DAY

HOME TEAM

PT CRUISER

OFFICE COUCH

FRESHMAN
DYE JOB

CAN OF BEANS

VEGAS CARPET

TOTALLY EXTRA

CREATE WITH YOUR RIGHT BRAIN!

Draw a self-portrait (if you have a mirror handy) or a portrait of someone else (if you have a friend handy)… but only use your right brain to do it. How? By only looking at the subject, and not the paper. When you do that, you'll stop the left brain from piping up with critiques, judgments, and any other get-you-in-your-head suggestions. So keep your eyes ONLY on the subject you're drawing, and no peeking! You might be surprised at how quickly and easily your right brain can crank out a fun and playful, Picasso-rivaling portrait. Now try drawing something else the same way (pro tip: pets make excellent right-brain subjects), and for a real good time— have someone else draw you, with their right brain!

INSPO-GRAM

Light up your imagination with the brilliant orange flames of sacral inspiration and create some impromptu back stories for the folks in the photos below. And, if you have fun, take this show on the road and play it with friends wherever old photos are found (museums and/or the internet).

WHAT'S THIS WOMAN'S NAME?

_____

_____

_____

WHAT DOES SHE LOVE?

_____

_____

_____

HOW DID THESE TWO MEET?

_____

_____

_____

WHAT DO THEY ARGUE ABOUT?

_____

_____

_____

WHAT'S THE NAME OF THIS BAND?

_____

_____

_____

WHAT'S THEIR FIRST ALBUM?

_____

_____

_____

BASK IN THIS . . .

Fill in the blanks to weave a personalized meditation, then sit quietly and envision the scenario in your mind's eye, letting it play out for as long as you want (pressing emergencies excepted).

Imagine you're watching the sunset in _____.
(your ultimate sunset spot)

The orange glow is contagious, and begins to gather on everything. You see an iridescent, orange sparkling light

around your _____.
(description of fave article of clothing)

From your naval, a beam of light shoots out to meet the sunset, and begins to intertwine with it. In the center of

the sun, _____ appears, and reaches out to you.
(name of your biggest hero)

They hand you a/n _____and say "I know you are _____."
(object used to create something)   (positive adjective)

You accept the gift. You ponder the meaning. You shamelessly bask in the glowiness of it all...

THE PLEASURE IS ALL YOURS

If you wanna open your sacral chakra (AKA your pleasure center), you've gotta get down with all things pleasurable. Use the prompts below to create your own personal pleasure checklist…then make it your mission to enjoy one thing from the list each day this week. And if that goes well, there's no saying you gotta stop…you're the pleasure boss of you!

Food that makes my stomach smile:

_____

Movie that makes me laugh more than most things:

_____

Song that makes me want to go all Baby in *Dirty Dancing*:

_____

Person who makes me feel good about myself whenever we hang out:

_____

Place I enjoy watching the world go by:

_____

Activity I've only done once, but really want to do again:

_____

Something I've always wanted to try:

_____

An animal (other than my own pets) that I'd like to meet/hold/snuggle:

_____

Event coming up that's a little out of the box for me, but sounds very intriguing:

_____

Book I totally want to read:

_____

Excuse to get dressed up all fancy-like:

_____

Something I love to cook or bake:

_____

Something crafty I've always wanted to make:

_____

A nature-y place I love to walk:

_____

An adventure that puts a few butterflies in my tummy:

_____

A treasured friend I'm gonna call for a long-overdue chat:

_____

A homemade gift I can make for no reason, then give to someone as soon as there's a reason:

_____

Someone I can write a good old-fashioned, pen-and-paper letter to:

_____

HEY, NEEDS! 'SUP?
(WE HAVEN'T TALKED IN A WHILE . . .)

No one is born with a talent for gracefully articulating their needs (evidence: our first months are mostly spent screaming). It's something we learn (and hopefully get better at) along the way. Are you being honest with yourself (and your significant other(s)) about what you need to be a happy, fulfilled, warm, and loving partner rather than a screaming baby?

In my ideal relationship, I would (mostly, if not always) feel:

_____

_____

_____

Some things the other person could do that would make me feel this way (rather than keep me guessing):

_____

_____

_____

PERSONAL PERSONALS!

Remember how awkward, strange, confusing and/or borderline humiliating it used to feel to try and navigate relationships when you were younger/less worldly/not the most mature (or um—like last week)? Oh. Us neither. Cool cool cool. Well, regardless of your aptitude for excelling at the romantic nitty gritty, chances are you've improved along the way. And you can prove it by using the blanks to complete these dating profiles . . . one from the POV of a "past YOU" (pick a specific age or stage!), and one from "now-ish YOU." How has your view of yourself changed? How about what you're looking for? OMG WHAT DOES THIS IMPLY ABOUT THE FUTURE?

PAST YOU

_____ seeks _____
(adjective/noun)   (adjective/noun)

for _____ ,
         (verb ending in ing)

_____ , and lots of
   (verb ending in ing)

_____ .
      (behavior ending in ing)

Only reply if you're _____
                              (adjective)

and _____ .
         (adjective)

PRESENT YOU

_____ seeks _____
(adjective/noun)   (adjective/noun)

for _____ ,
         (verb ending in ing)

_____ , and lots of
   (verb ending in ing)

_____ .
      (behavior ending in ing)

Only reply if you're _____
                              (adjective)

and _____ .
         (adjective)

VICE BUSTER!

Give yourself a gold (or pink, or purple, or blunt-pencil-from-the-back-of-the-drawer) hand-drawn star for each vice you resist this week in the chart below.

THINGS I'D RATHER **NOT** HABITUALLY EAT, DRINK, SMOKE, DO, SAY, BE AROUND							
List any/all vices below.	MONDAY	TUESDAY	WEDNESDAY	THURSDAY	FRIDAY	SATURDAY	SUNDAY

OK, now show those vices who's boss by drawing a (much bigger) star for each good habit you nail!

THINGS THAT MAKE ME HEALTHIER, SMARTER, BETTER, KINDER, THE SORT OF PERSON WHO GIVES MYSELF INNER HIGH FIVES (VS. SHAMING FINGER WAGS)							
List any/all ways to be my best (or better-ish) self.	MONDAY	TUESDAY	WEDNESDAY	THURSDAY	FRIDAY	SATURDAY	SUNDAY

SOLAR PLEXUS

With the help of the solar plexus chakra, we begin to see ourselves as an individual, rather than just a stream of astral energy walking around among billions of other streams of astral energy. As beautiful as that energy party sounds, if you didn't have a solar plexus chakra, you wouldn't have a sense of where you end and the rest of all that swirling, cosmic ether begins. What would they put on your driver's license? The solar plexus is a great partner to the chakra that comes before it (hey there, sacral!). If the sacral chakra is the spark, the solar plexus is the fuel. This puppy knows how to transform raw inspiration into tangible action so you can use your opinions to shape the world around you (or at least redecorate your apartment). The solar plexus is the chakra of identity, power, and will.

WHEN YOUR SOLAR PLEXUS IS RIGHT:
You're on fire with confidence, but not ego mania. You're inspired to actively pursue goals, while still prioritizing personal relationships (in other words, you're an opinionated, driven, non-sociopath). You speak directly, but not insultingly, and you're secure with your place in the world.

"No I didn't see that—I only check social media once a day."

WHEN YOUR SOLAR PLEXUS IS BLOCKED:
You'll feel small and powerless, or completely devoid of ambition. You might make lots of plans but show zero follow through, or just feel lost and aimless—a sailboat without its sail.

"Sorry, I would have gotten off the couch but I couldn't because my ideas about how to stand up are all stupid."

WHEN YOUR SOLAR PLEXUS IS OVERACTIVE:
It can bring out the worst in even the best. You'll operate on manipulation, single-mindedness, too much ego, and a need to control everyone and everything around you.

"What do you mean I have a dictator complex? You're fired."

KEY CONCEPTS:
- Personal Power
- Identity
- Opinion
- Intellect
- Action
- Ambition
- Will

LOCATION:
At the Navel (though these days lots of people think of it as a few inches below the sternum)

TO OPEN AND BALANCE YOUR SOLAR PLEXUS:
Color: Yellow
Essential Oils: Juniper, Geranium, Rosemary, Clary Sage
Stones:
- Overactive = Sapphire/Emerald
- Blocked = Topaz/Yellow Tourmaline
- For General Balance = Citrine

Yoga Pose: Camel
Musical Key: E
Food: Lemons, Bananas, Pineapples, Corn, Squash, Turmeric, Ginger

SOLAR PLEXUS CHAKRA PLAYLIST (SONGS IN THE KEY OF E):

"Africa" (Toto)
"Isn't She Lovely" (Stevie Wonder)
"Yellow Ledbetter" (Pearl Jam)
"Soul Man" (Sam & Dave)
"Single Ladies" (Beyonce)
"Sympathy for the Devil" (The Rolling Stones)
"Norwegian Wood" (The Beatles)
"Heart of Glass" (Blondie)
"Just Dance" (Lady Gaga)

KNOW THYSELF/VES IN 3, 2, 1...

Ever wish you could know what your subconscious is saying about you behind your back? Your wish just came true! This is a game that's all about digging into unconscious symbolism to help you know yourself in a way that's usually only reserved for talented therapists and lucid dreams. It takes all of three minutes to master, and its wisdom can be reproduced wherever a pen and a napkin reside. In other words, you're about to become a dive-bar life coach.

TO PLAY:
Follow the prompts below, and be sure to always go with the first thing that comes to mind. No second-guessing or mind-changing or switching it up. What pops up doesn't need to make sense to you—it does make sense to your subconscious, and that's all that matters. Because at the end of the day, aren't we all just unwilling puppets of our subconscious? Here we go...

STEP ONE
Think of an animal. Any animal—but it has to be the first one that comes to mind.

Animal: _____

Name three character traits that capture its essence ("clever," "nurturing," "wild," "frightened," "beautiful," etc.)

_____

_____

STEP TWO
Think of another animal. (No self-edits!)

Animal: _____

Aaaaand...three things that capture its essence.

_____

_____

STEP THREE
Think of another animal. (Yes, again! And quickly!)

Animal: _____

Yep, yep, yep. Three things that capture its essence.

_____

_____

YOUR ANIMAL PICKS ANALYZED:

The first trio of traits represents how you see yourself. This is your subconscious way of describing yourself, or how you want to be perceived.

The second animal represents how others see you.

The third animal represents how you really are.

ISLANDS IN THE STREAM (OF CONSCIOUSNESS):
(A GUIDED FILL-IN-THE-BLANK MEDITATION)

Imagine yourself on a simple sailboat, far out in the ocean. The boat is strong and sturdy, and it's a beautiful day. There aren't any threats of white squalls, perfect storms, or other Hollywood ocean-horrors. Just a safe solitary cruise through the infinite blue. The boat's main sail is a perfect symbol of your personality: on it is a giant picture of _____ . As you sail,
(something inspirational)

you realize that a bright yellow beam of light is shooting out of your solar plexus, guiding the boat's direction. It moves easily, smoothly, and swiftly in whatever direction you "think" it…and that makes you feel _____ . Hanging onto that feeling of _____ ,
(pleasant emotion/feeling)   (pleasant emotion/feeling)

you begin to move faster. A string of islands appears on the horizon, and you can see that each one holds a very distinct possibility. They each radiate an emotional quality, and as you get closer you can see those qualities more clearly. The first island is a place you don't want to go. The emotional quality it radiates is _____ . It is the sort of place where people _____
(pleasing emotion)   (verb)

and _____ , and everyone is a _____ . The slogan of the island is
(verb)   (name of job)

"_____." Not for you. The middle island seems exactly like
(fun, uplifting phrase)

where your life is now. The emotional quality it radiates is _____ . You can see people
(pleasing emotion)

_____ and _____ ; their main goal seems to be _____ .
(verbing)   (verbing)   (noun)

There are people waiting for you, who can bring you straight to _____ for
(location)

_____ . They all seem _____ with their lives. The third island is
(activity, job, or event)   (emotion)

unlike your present life. It carries an emotional quality of _____ . It seems _____
(noun)   (adjective)

but also _____ . It looks like everyone there is _____ and _____ ,
(adjective)   (verbing)   (verbing)

and the main goal of every day is to _____ . There are people waiting to welcome
(awesome thing)

you there, too, and they show you that if you go there you will instantly have _____
(lifelong dream/goal)

and be _____ . They have a job waiting for you as someone who _____ ,
(adjective)   (coolest career ever)

and they tell you that your days will be filled with _____ and _____ .
(something awesome)   (favorite food/drink/thing)

YOU CAN GUIDE THE SAILBOAT IN ANY DIRECTION YOU CHOOSE. WHICH WAY DO YOU GO?
LET YOUR MEDITATION PLAY OUT, AND ENVISION WHAT HAPPENS.

MY OPINIONS ON JUST ABOUT EVERYTHING

The solar plexus chakra is where you separate yourself from the pack. It's the chakra that expresses opinions and will—and possibly gets you into dinner table arguments when not used responsibly. You might be surprised to discover that when you stop to think about it, you can find a strong opinion on just about everything in the world. Below is a list of things you might have thought you didn't really care about…challenge yourself to write down a specific opinion for each one. If your first reaction is ambivalence or apathy, push past it until you find a tiny spark of positive/negative feelings. Then fan those flames to get to the good stuff! Your solar plexus chakra is ready to remind you that finding your voice is a practice worth practicing.

(Note: if you're having trouble getting started, feel free to choose from the cheat sheet at the bottom of the page. If that feels like cheating, then congratulations! That's also an opinion!)

Key lime pie: _____

The UFC: _____

Train trips: _____

Reclining chairs: _____

Political rallies: _____

Pinterest: _____

Wealth: _____

Pajamas-as-clothes: _____

Internet startups: _____

Pixar: _____

Incense: _____

Puns: _____

Marriage: _____

The desert: _____

Goat memes: _____

New Year's parties: _____

Star Wars: _____

Dachsunds: _____

Competitive baking: _____

Cold soups: _____

Sleeping in: _____

Camouflage: _____

Treehouses: _____

Buffets: _____

Mini golf: _____

Pigeons: _____

Tea: _____

Ellipses (…) : _____

CHEAT SHEET (IN CASE YOUR OPINION ENGINE NEEDS A LITTLE JUMP-START):

- Inspiring
- Useless
- Not as good as you remember
- Overrated
- Underrated
- Romantic

- So dramatic
- Intimidating
- A total turn-on
- More expensive than they should be
- An impressive invention

- Confusing
- Pretentious
- A pleasant surprise
- Insightful
- Envy-inducing
- Not to be given as a gift

EGO CHECK-LIST

Confidence is great, but if we don't keep our ego in check with a little bit of humility and gratitude, we can run the risk of becoming an arrogance monster.

In the spaces below, you'll write down four different compliments about yourself. Don't worry about sounding cocky—you'll be able to check your ego in a minute. Once you've made your list, ruminate on all the people you know (or role models you would love to know) who helped inspire, nurture, and foster those qualities in you (either through personal help or totally-impersonal-but-still-totally-valid inspiration). Notice how you couldn't have gotten to where you are alone. After all, it takes a village to raise an out-of-this-world superstar!

FOUR THINGS I LOVE ABOUT ME:

1. _____

2. _____

3. _____

4. _____

HERE'S WHO I CAN CREDIT FOR INSPIRING/FOSTERING/NURTURING QUALITY #1:

_____
_____
_____

HERE'S WHO I CAN CREDIT FOR INSPIRING/FOSTERING/NURTURING QUALITY #2:

_____
_____
_____

HERE'S WHO I CAN CREDIT FOR INSPIRING/FOSTERING/NURTURING QUALITY #3:

_____
_____
_____

HERE'S WHO I CAN CREDIT FOR INSPIRING/FOSTERING/NURTURING QUALITY #4:

_____
_____
_____

GOAL GET 'EM!

At the top of the mountain, write a goal that you have. This can be as big as your ultimate career achievement, or as small as "learning to draw something that isn't a stick figure."

Break the mountain climb into smaller, much-more-manageable hikes (or short strolls even), by writing the steps it will take to get there. When you complete each step, put a check mark next to it. When you get to the top, hire a trumpeter to underscore your box-checking with ostentatious fanfare. Then take a hard-earned nap.

SOLAR PLEXUS POWERS ACTIVATE!

It's been proven* by science**, that repeating mantras and saying affirmations aloud helps make them come true and actually stick. Activate your personal potency by saying the following phrases out loud, in a very convincingly confident voice, while standing in a power stance. Take your pick from the poses below.

THE WONDER WOMAN
Listen up, doubters! I claim my personal power and let it burn like a blindingly bright supernova. Sorry for your blindness. Not sorry for my power.

THE SUPER MAN
I achieve everything I set my mind to. Once I decide I want it, it's as good as done. The only thing left to do is the doing, which is way more fun than sitting around and waiting (or self-hating). Doing powers, ACTIVATE!

THE MORE-CONFIDENT-THAN-AVERAGE REGULAR PERSON
I deserve to have the life I want, and I call it into being. That's right, Dream Life! I see you, I know you, and I'm declaring myself entwined with you. (That's you, right Dream Life? Sorry, you look different with that haircut.)

*Suggested
**Some people somewhere who did some research of some sort

POWER SHIELD

Knowing who you are is great, but celebrating who you are is even better! When we stand proudly in our personal power, we draw the strength that allows us to feel impenetrable—even in the face of internet trolls! Create the perfect (or perfectly imperfect!) emblem of your personal power by drawing (or pasting pictures of) each category on your shield. Then spend the week relishing your newfound invincibility.

QUADRANT 1:
A motto you swear by.

QUADRANT 2:
An animal that, if you could, you would have by your side at all times (ideally in a costume).

QUADRANT 3:
An environment that brings you peace, strength, joy or other objective pluses.

QUADRANT 4:
Three adjectives that describe your best qualities on your best days.

I'VE COME A LONG WAY, BABY!

Use this map to reflect on the places life's already taken you while you were pursuing your dreams (or where you perhaps already made your wildest dreams come true!).

You can include big milestones (like graduating from high school/college/international spy school; first kiss/job/Nobel Prize; having a kid/adopting your fur baby…)—or little moments that meant a lot (e.g., meeting your idol, seeing Les Mis for the first time…). At each stop on the winding road, make some specific notes about the kind of "you" you were at the time.

THINGS LIKE...
* Where you were in the world (literally or figuratively).
* What you felt like (e.g., confused, happy, excited-but-scared).
* Adjectives you'd use to describe yourself (eg; dorky, awkward, perfect in every way).
* Something you learned (perhaps the hard way)
* A new identity you adopted—or shed (e.g., "the goth years")

Extra credit (not to mention extra fun): Add a pic of yourself from each era.
There's really no better way to be amazed at how far you've come. Congrats.

WRITE A LOVE LIST TO YOUR WEEK!

This week or last—you pick! (But don't tell the other one. That never goes well.)

WHAT ARE SOME...

* Kickass things you did/saw/read/heard?
* Things you learned (no matter how small)?
* People you were glad to have around?
* Decisions you made?
* Goals you worked towards? (Even if it wasn't very noticeable from the outside, because TBH it rarely is.)
* Connections you felt?
* Public figures you admired?

NOW, WHAT ARE YOU GONNA TAKE WITH YOU MOVING FORWARD? (AKA WRITE SOME INTENTIONS FOR NEXT WEEK!)

"I will _____

_____."
(something you will do, however big or small)

"I roll out the welcome mat for _____

_____."
(emotions/experiences, people you want to call in)

"I unapologetically ditch _____

_____."
(behaviors/attitudes/experiences you want to let go of)

POWER PUZZLES

Confidence is a key to opening life's doors, but when it tips into arrogance it can close them in a hurry. The trick is to keep some humility in the back of your mind, so you can strike an oh-so-happy medium.

Use the clues to help you solve the word puzzles below, and you'll reveal some phrases that pair well with a flowing, glowing solar plexus chakra. Solve all three and win a special prize*!

CLUE: TAKE OUT SELFISHNESS, AND WHAT ARE YOU LEFT WITH?

S E A L H F E I S A H
L N T E H Y S E S G O

CLUE: THERE IS NO "I" IN...

W I I E I C I A I I I N I T I I
A I L I I I I W I I I A I Y I I S I
G I O I A I I L O I N I I E I

CLUE: REMOVE YOUR DESIRE TO CONTROL...

Y A D O E U L I G R H
D T F E U S L I W O R
R K I E N G E T N O
V C I O N R O N T M
R E O N L T

*Useful tidbits of wisdom, applicable daily.

Answers: 1. A Healthy ego; 2. We can't always go alone; 3. A delightful working environment

GETTING LIT...

We all have a personal furnace that gives us the gusto to GO without giving up. It's the fire that burns in our belly (ahem, solar plexus) and makes us really care about the things we pursue. It's helpful to check in and remind ourselves of the things that add fuel to that furnace (pastimes, passions, interests, goals, the lifelong pursuit of a charitable cause)—so that, any time we're feeling a little less-than-lit, we can make a constant choice to stoke that sucker and inspire our fire. Otherwise, these marshmallows are useless ...

FIVE THINGS THAT REALLY FAN MY FLAMES:

1. _____

2. _____

3. _____

4. _____

5. _____

I'm most passionate about _____

and _____ .

I'm happiest when I'm _____

_____

or _____ .

I feel like my personal talent wheelhouse is

_____ .

I wish the world would _____

_____

_____ .

I'm on a mission to _____

_____

_____ .

I'm intrigued by _____

_____ .

I bet I could someday learn how to _____

_____ , _____ ,

_____ ,

and/or _____ .

I've got an eyeball on future trips to _____

_____ and _____ .

I'm inspired by _____

_____

and I'd love to adopt their qualities of _____

_____ ,

_____ ,

and maybe _____ .

Above all else, the most important thing is that I

_____

_____

_____

MAKE YOUR OWN POWER TOTEMS

Fill in the blanks and create a power trio of personalized emblems, representing your strength, power, and all-around awesomeness. Once you're done, tuck these thoughtfully crafted images in a mental pocket so can access them whenever you're feeling down or in doubt.

HERE'S HOW IT MIGHT LOOK:

* I am an <u>elephant</u>, standing on a <u>monster truck</u>, holding a <u>scepter</u>.
* I am a <u>redwood forest</u>, emanating a powerful <u>teal</u> glow, which spreads across the land and make everyone it touches start <u>laughing so hard your face hurts</u>.
* I am a <u>comet</u>. I ride through space on a <u>jet ski</u> to the song <u>"Africa" by Toto</u>, and I leave behind me a wake of glittering <u>cookie dough</u> that spells out <u>"you are magic."</u>

I am a/n _____ , standing on a/n _____ , holding a _____ .
              (animal)   (symbol of strength)   (cool object)

I am a/n _____ , emanating a powerful _____ glow, which spreads across the
        (large feature of nature)   (favorite color)

land and makes everyone it touches start _____ .
                                         ("ing" verb—an activity that you find awesome)

I am a/n _____ . I ride through space on a _____ , to the song
          (celestial object)   (favorite form of transportation)

_____ , and I leave behind me a wake of glittering _____
   (song you never get tired of)   (something you'd like to get as a gift)

that spell(s) out "_____ ."
                    (your favorite compliment to receive)

OK, NOW DRAW IT!

My Power Totem

NICE TO MEET YOU, HABIT. YOU NEW HERE?

Scientific rumor has it that it takes forty days to create a new habit. That might sound like a long time, but if you think about it, it's really not. Forty days is just over a month—or the length of time it takes to get through half an issue of *The New Yorker*.

Use the chart below to outline some new habits you'd like to adopt. Then actually do 'em (aha—you knew there was a catch!) every day for forty days as an experiment. Feel free to set yourself free on day forty-one. But who knows, maybe you'll surprise yourself and keep going … science for the win! Pro tip: Start small, and don't do too many at once—you're still human, after all. (At least for the next forty days.)

SMALL HABITS (e.g., drinking ten glasses of water per day, making your bed, not dropping F bombs in public)	BIGGER HABITS (e.g., exercising every day, reading at least one chapter of a book per day, not looking at the news for at least an hour after you wake up)	BIGGEST HABITS (e.g., training for a marathon, writing a novel, giving up sugar)

ANAHATA (HEART) CHAKRA

The heart chakra marks our evolutionary leap into the first level of the four "higher" chakras—that is, the chakras that are less about human affairs, my food, my relationships, my promotion that should never have gone to Kevin, and more about our connection, our oneness, our understanding of spiritual truths…and that even includes Kevin. The heart chakra takes us straight out of our own personal B.S. and into a zone of compassion, forgiveness, and generosity. It is the chakra of unconditional love, as felt by anyone who has a child.*

WHEN YOUR HEART'S RIGHT:
You'll enjoy intimacy with an open heart and no nagging echoes of chaotic relationships past. You'll forgive easily, communicate with empathy, and give love and support to your nearest and dearest with no expectation of return.

"You got me a gift? I told you—giving to you is my gift."

WHEN YOUR HEART'S OVERACTIVE:
Side effects include jealousy, stinginess, or excessive self-interest. It can also cause you to play the martyr card, giving excessively to anyone and everyone around you, without the boundaries needed to maintain your own self-care.

"Well if I stop to sleep then who will feed the city's pigeons?!"

WHEN YOUR HEART'S BLOCKED:
Life will play all your least favorite hits: sadness, insecurity, mistrust, and emotional meltdowns over everything from work emails to romcom movie trailers. Not the funnest days/weeks/months/years on the calendar.

"I can't come in to work today. I'm crying into my oatmeal again."

KEY CONCEPTS:
* Love
* Trust
* Compassion
* Empathy
* Connection

LOCATION:
Center of the Chest

TO OPEN AND BALANCE YOUR HEART:
Color: Green (also sometimes depicted as pink)
Essential Oils: Rose, Neroli, Melissa (AKA Lemon Balm)
Stones:
* Overactive = Pink Topaz
* Blocked = Peridot
* For General Balance = Rose Quartz

Yoga Pose: Cobra
Musical Key: F
Food: Lettuce, Spinach, Kale, Mint, Green Pepper, Cucumber, Celery

HEART CHAKRA PLAYLIST (SONGS IN THE KEY OF D):

"Open Your Heart" (Madonna)
"Let's Go Crazy" (Prince)
"Crazy in Love" (Beyoncé)
"Just the Way You Are" (Bruno Mars)
"Call Me" (Blondie)
"All Day and All of the Night" (The Kinks)
"Such Great Heights" (The Postal Service)
"Mr. Blue Sky" (ELO)
"At Last" (Ella Fitzgerald)
"Tapestry" (Carole King)
"You Make My Dreams Come True" (Hall & Oates)

*Or a pet.**
**Or who's ever seen video footage of a baby elephant playing.

I LOVE MYSELF BECAUSE...

When we're walking around with an open, loving heart, we love to give glittery, glowing goodness to everyone around us. But sometimes, in the quest to show that love to others, we forget to give some glitter to ourselves. Use the blanks below to remind yourself just what it is that makes you so darn lovable. And remember, when you give goodness to yourself, you have more goodness to give others, and that is a pretty glittery party trick.

I'm good at _____ ,

_____ ,

and _____ .
(come on, you can think of a third)

I'm someone other people can turn to when they

need _____ .

A secret inner quality (or talent) I have that I don't

share with that many people is _____

_____ .

I've done some difficult things in my life. Like _____

_____ , and _____ ,

and _____ .
(yes, emotional journeys count)

I have some pretty cool dreams. For instance, I want

to see _____ ,

do _____ ,

and if there's time, learn _____ .

I notice and appreciate special qualities in other

people. Like _____ ,

_____ ,

and _____ .
(why is it always easier to think of a third thing about them?)

In my life, _____

is a priority, and I always take the time to _____

_____ .

So. I may not be the most_____

person in the game, but I am definitely _____

_____ , _____ ,

_____ , _____ ,

_____ , _____ ,
(go for it—list them all)

_____ ,

and _____ .
(woohoo—yay, you!)

WOW. YOU'RE REALLY GREAT AT GIVING COMPLIMENTS.

In order to be open, a heart has to be willing to be vulnerable. That usually means (in addition to open-mouth sobbing at the end of animal reunion videos) being able to show kindness to others with free-wheeling abandon, no neuroses invited!

The name of the game is Compliment Parade. We're talking back-to-back compliments blaring out the love like a boisterous cavalcade of holiday marching bands. To play, all you have to do is set a time limit*, and for the duration of that time give a genuine compliment to everyone you pass. Sound challenging? It won't be once you start making everyone's day!

THREE COMPLIMENTS I GAVE TODAY:

TO A FRIEND:

TO A STRANGER:

TO SOMEONE I'M NOT PARTICULARLY IN LOVE WITH (AKA CAN'T REMOTELY STAND):

*Or a space limit (e.g., "While I'm in this store";"On my walk through the office this morning"; "By the time I reach the other end of this Costco. Is there an end to this Costco?").

RE-TELL IT LIKE IT IS!

We're all living inside of the stories we tell ourselves about our lives and the people we bump up against (e.g., loved ones, coworkers, friends, Facebook friends, their Facebook friends, and so on). The thing is, those inside-our-head stories usually sound a lot more negative than the objective, realistic, not-riled-up-by-that-annoying-conversation truth. So what about changing your storytelling style?

Reframing your narrative is a handy little tactic, and it works like this. You tell an account of the same event, as seen through a more positive, understanding, compassionate lens. The effect is twofold! One: you get to stop playing the victim and move on to better, meatier roles. Two: you get to work on your compassion and empathy, by imagining what the other person was up to.

Something that made me feel hurt, small, or anything else unsavory:

_____

_____

_____

_____ .

What the other person did wrong:

_____

_____

_____

_____ .

Some potential reasons they did what they did, that I could potentially understand:

_____

_____

_____

_____ .

Something good this event gave/taught/reminded me:

_____

_____

_____

_____ .

A positive spin I could put on the whole thing (even if I'm not actually feeling it yet):

_____

_____

_____

_____ .

What I'll try to take with me for next time:

_____

_____

_____

_____ .

POSITIVITY Rx

The Buddhist lovingkindness meditation is a great antidote to bitterness and resentment of all shapes and sizes. Thinking loving thoughts about someone is sort of like shining a flashlight into a dark room. The light erases darkness wherever it goes, but the darkness can't fight back and overtake the light. Uh-oh, darkness—looks like you lose again! This meditation practice involves extending kind thoughts not only to people you love, but also to…(cue dark dramatic music)…people you hate. Take 5–30 minutes and try it on for size—you might be surprised at how effective it is!

HERE'S HOW:

In this meditation, you'll envision four people from your life. Not all at once. You'll actually go one step at a time, but here's the cast of characters…

1. Someone you adore/revere/would jump into a volcano for
2. Someone you like/respect/would like to invite over for dinner if you both could find the time
3. Someone you feel totally neutral about; like, maybe you rode in their Lyft once
4. Someone you completely and utterly disdain/despise/would like to vomit a contagious disease onto

Envision the first person from the list. See them in all their kind, beautiful—can't believe they sent you a care package when you were sick—glory. Once you see them clearly in your mind, repeat this wish for them over and over:

"MAY THEY BE HEALTHY."

"MAY THEY BE HAPPY."

"MAY THEY BE FREE FROM SUFFERING OF ANY KIND."

Spend a few minutes repeating those wishes, and when you feel that you've sufficiently covered that person in ooey-gooey loving light, move on to the next.

You'll repeat the process for each person on the list.

Remember, NO CHEATING. You need to give just as much genuine well-wishing to the person you disdain as you did to the person you revere. And who knows… they may be secretly doing the same meditation about you. Or not. Either way. Good vibes only and whatnot.

Warning: may cause pervasive, life-long happiness and an increase in meaningful, loving relationships. And, in some extreme cases may lead to world peace.

RANDOM ACTS OF KINDNESS BINGO!

Complete a row in any direction to earn your cred as a Captain of Kindness. Or, to really go for it, cover the whole board...what a showoff!

Write a thank-you note to a coworker. (Expect nothing in return.)	Bake homemade cookies and give them away.	Babysit for a friend. (For FREE.)	Send a hand-written letter to someone you know.
Talk to a homeless person. Ask their name. Get them something they need.	Tip generously. (Like 30 percent generously.)	Give someone a hug. (They probably need it more than you think.)	Pick up litter that isn't yours.
Make a personalized mix or playlist for an old friend.	Compliment someone in front of their boss.	Bring soup or other goodies to someone who isn't feeling well.	Hold the door for at least five people.
Give a stranger flowers.	Walk a friend's dog.	Feed an empty parking meter.	Give up your seat— or randomly pay the toll for the car behind you.

NOT FEELING THE LOVE (OR COMPASSION)?

If your heart chakra's been zombiefied, you don't need to take drastic measures to bring it back from the dead. Just keep it super simple and give compassion a try. Start small. You might try listening to a long-winded complaint from a long-winded coworker, or letting your eighty-year-old neighbor describe the difference between the air quality in Ohio and the air quality in Arizona, or you might call that family member you haven't talked to since the holidays even though you get your news from different corners of the internet and you know they're dying to dismantle your reality. Whatever the person, whatever their situation, just genuinely lend a sympathetic ear to someone about something important they're going through—something that's got nothing to do with you.

> **TIPS, TRICKS, AND COMPASSION-HACKS:**
> * Ask follow-up questions.
> * Prove your genuine interest by nodding, saying "mm-hm," and (when possible) repeating details (e.g., names, locations).
> * If asked, offer thoughtful advice.
> * Support their point of view, even if you "know" they're "wrong."
> * Tell no one. (The compassion is sorta defeated when it turns into gossip.)

HAPPINESS IS A WARM AND UTTERLY GENUINE SMILE

There's a new drug in town, and it's called the endorphins you release when someone smiles at you. That's right—someone smiles, and you get high. OK, maybe it's a tiny, imperceptible, microscopic high—but it's healthy, which is a rarity these days, so that counts for something, right? The best part is, the person who smiles catches some of that sweet, sweet endorphin rush too. And the even best-er part is that you're both sharing a very positive, very genuine moment of human connection and open-heartedness, *oh my god is that a rainbow?* So let's go ahead and turn this positivity spiral into a game! The object of the game is to see how many people you can get to smile at you today. And the winner of the game is, duh, everyone.

FRIEND = 1 POINT
PERSON YOU'VE MET ONCE OR TWICE = 2 POINTS
STRANGER = 4 POINTS
ANNOYING STRANGER = 12 POINTS
STRANGER WHO HAPPENS TO BE A ZOMBIE = 100 POINTS

DATE/SCORE:

_____ / _____

_____ / _____

_____ / _____

LETTING GO OF WHATEVER AWFUL ICKINESS REMAINS FROM THAT THING THAT PERSON DID THAT BROKE ME...

You can't always achieve closure with people who have, well, closed your heart. You may have drawn a much-needed boundary between the two of you; you may have moved on from them completely; or perhaps they took your Playstation, changed their phone number, and moved to Texas. Regardless of what stands between you, it can be helpful, healing, and heart-massaging to write them a (pretend) letter that you'll never (under any circumstances) send to them. This gives you the freedom to say everything you want to say…and once you freely get the ickiness out, you can truly and freely let go.

Dear _____ ,

I really didn't appreciate it when you _____ .

It made me think you were _____ , _____ ,
and a total _____ .

But I don't like feeling _____ and _____ because
those feelings really don't feel like me at all.

I much prefer the idea of being _____ , _____ ,
and/or _____ .

I've resisted forgiving you, because _____
_____ .

But I realize now that's silly, because I'm an adult who has my own _____ life to live.

The best way to forgive you is to remember that I too am imperfect. One time I _____
_____ , and another time I _____ .

At certain times in my life I have been _____ , _____ , and (some of my exes might even say) _____ .

So, I can only hope that other people are out there forgiving me right now, and not imagining me as some sort of _____ for the rest of my life.

I like the idea that they've forgiven me, and I like the idea that I get to move on from my past screw-ups so that I can become a better, wiser, more _____ person.

So I'm extending the same forgiveness to you. I'm forgiving you for the _____ you caused me, and I'm letting all of the _____ go.

It's been really tiresome carrying it around, and it's actually affected my other relationships because at times it makes me _____ and _____ .

At the end of the day, life is short, and we're just silly, dumb little humans trying our silly, dumb little best. So I forgive you, _____ .

I forgive you, and I wish you all the _____ , _____ , and _____ in the world.

Can you believe what a _____ person I am? (Honestly, I think you might have blown it.)

> **"HOLDING ONTO RESENTMENT IS LIKE DRINKING POISON AND WAITING FOR THE OTHER PERSON TO DIE."**
>
> —attributed to Buddha, Nelson Mandela, and many others…but the origins are unknown. Perhaps it's just a universal truth?

MY DATE WITH ME

In order to accept love from others, you first need to show love to yourself. And what better way to do that than by taking yourself on a date? Meaning: you and you, and no one else. If you're not the spend-time-alone type, this'll be a good chance to practice alone-but-not-lonely time, by doing something that lights you up and makes you feel warmed and fuzzed. If you're the constant-loner type, this is a good chance to get a little creative—to show off for yourself a little and treat your alone time to something extra decadent or out of the ordinary. Now go have fun, you two! And don't do anything you wouldn't do!

THIS WEEK, I TOOK MYSELF ON A DATE. YAY!

Here's what I did:

_____

_____

Here's what I did to make it extra AF:

_____

_____

Here's what I noticed/thought/felt about it all:

_____

_____

Most amazing moment:

_____

_____

Some observations I noticed about me:

_____

_____

The obvious pros (and wow, there were a lot):

_____

_____

The much subtler, and very manageable cons:

_____

_____

Is it a match? Will I go on a date with me again? (Circle one.)

Heck Yeah! * Sure * Probs Maybe *

Def Probably * Lemme Think About It

Some ideas for future Me-Dates:

_____

_____

_____

_____

HEY THANKS, LIFE!

Spending a few minutes each day writing down things you're grateful for can improve your mood and open your heart. Big or small, it doesn't matter!

So start—right here, right now!—then go out and get yourself a colorfully designed notebook that speaks to your heart (and/or was on sale), and make keeping a gratitude list/journal a new daily habit. Your heart chakra (and the humans in your regular orbit) will thank you. They might even journal about it.

BIG THINGS I'M THANKFUL FOR

LITTLE THINGS I'M THANKFUL FOR

EXPERIENCES I'M THANKFUL FOR

UNEXPECTED THINGS I'M THANKFUL FOR

PEOPLE I'M THANKFUL FOR

LIFE LESSONS I'M THANKFUL FOR

THROAT CHAKRA

Once you've gotten a handle on how best to do you (thanks, solar plexus!), and have nailed the whole caring-about-others thing (hey there, heart!), you're ready to responsibly foist your ideas onto everyone around you. As you can probably guess, the throat chakra is the home of your voice—though in this case that "voice" is your inner truth. When you're speaking your mind freely (and kindly) and living the life you want to live (with respect and good human-ness), then you're aligned with this mighty champ and inner spokesperson. The throat chakra shares a special connection with the sacral chakra, since the creativity that's fostered there helps us to amplify our voice in the world. This is the chakra of communication, self-expression, and life purpose, and it reminds us that there is nothing more important than authenticity.*

WHEN YOUR THROAT'S RIGHT:
You'll feel great about the career, art, trade, or who-cares-if-I-have-a-job path you're on. You'll be able to speak honestly without any fear of what others might think…and you definitely won't dim your light.

"I never knew that painting woodland creatures on accordions was an option, but I guess my destiny found me."

WHEN YOUR THROAT'S BLOCKED:
When it's blocked, you'll turn shy, introverted, perhaps even all cagey, like "Um. I have a thing. I'm going to a thing. Don't worry about it." You also might feel like you're not fulfilling your life's purpose—or that what you thought was your purpose is not fulfilling you.

"Hey. Original career path? I think we might need to break up…"

WHEN YOUR THROAT'S OVERACTIVE:
Your communication will suffer from too much… well…you. You'll tend to talk too much, listen too little, and use your words for harm instead of good (think: lying, gossiping, name-calling, secret-spilling, and frequent-yet-casual-reputation-tarnishing).

"Ohmygod. Did you see the way that total stranger just innocently smiled and opened the door for you? What a suck-up…"

KEY CONCEPTS:
* Communication
* Expression
* Honesty
* Voice
* Authenticity
* Purpose

LOCATION:
The Throat, Extending Through the Front and Back of the Neck

TO OPEN AND BALANCE YOUR THROAT:
Color: Turquoise
Essential Oils: Lavender, Chamomile, Peppermint
Stones:
* Overactive = Quartz
* Blocked = Blue/Yellow Topaz
* For General Balance = Turquoise/Chrysocolla

Yoga Pose: Bow
Musical Key: G
Food: Blueberries, Blackberries, Coconut Water, Raw Honey, Herbal Tea

THROAT CHAKRA PLAYLIST (SONGS IN THE KEY OF D):

"Come as You Are" (Nirvana)
"Wish You Were Here" (Pink Floyd)
"Creep" (Radiohead)
"Another One Bites the Dust" (Queen)
"Tangled up in Blue" (Bob Dylan)
"L.O.V.E." (Nat King Cole)
"Take Me Out" (Franz Ferdinand)
"The Chain" (Fleetwood Mac)
"That's All" (Genesis)

*Not even reliable wifi.

SHOUT YOUR TRUTH

It's good (and healthy) to speak your mind. But it's also good to take a sec and listen to your heart. You know, take your heart out for a glass of rosé and really hear where it's at these days. Use the prompts below to have a mind-to-heart check-in … then don't doubt your truth, shout your truth! (Or at least think silently about your truth.)

I believe in _____ .

I know that _____ . (Like deep down in my toes know it.)

I'd totally fight for _____ .

I celebrate _____ .

I reject _____ .

I'd never _____ .

I strive to _____ .

I wish I _____ .

I wish the world _____ .

I just can't get behind _____ .

I'm utterly confused by _____ .

I'd throw down some serious cash to _____ .

Basically, I'm the sort of _____ who's all about _____

and _____ over _____ and _____ .

USE! YOUR! VOICE!

START SMALL
Sing in the shower, car, basement, or any other isolated locale (bank vault highly recommended, though only use it if you have access—this isn't worth a heist).

GO A BIT BIGGER
Shout/yell/loudly call "hello" into a canyon, off of a cliff, or from inside a cave.

AND BIGGER STILL
Scream, full force, for as long as you can, into a pillow. Repeat. Repeat again. Enjoy the endorphins.

AND BOOM! FINALLY
Sing loudly, publicly and with complete abandon (karaoke counts, though *a capella* earns a higher "brass balls" score). Film and post for ultimate proof that you have a voice and you're not afraid to use it (to potentially humiliate yourself). Pipe down, haters.

SLOGAN SLINGER

Quick question: what's the difference between you and all the people whose quotes appear on posters? Quick answer: someone wrote theirs down. OK, and also those people are/were super famous—but that doesn't mean their POV's are any more VIP than yours! Align with your throatiest opinions, and use the quote generator below to create a quotable quota of quirky quips.

"Never be mad at _____.
(something you love, even a small thing)

It's/They're what makes the world _____."
(verb—something you like to do)

"We have to forgive the _____ people and the
(negative adjective)

_____ of the world. They might not be
(plural noun—something you think is gross)

_____ or inspiring _____, but they
("ing" action you think is important)   (positive emotion)

remind the rest of us how lucky we are to be _____
(positive adjective)

_____."
("ing" action you think is important)

"If I could turn _____
(phrase you hate hearing)   into

_____ I'd do it every time."
(something people should say more often)

LIFE AT A GLANCE

So you've got a job that fulfills your daily/weekly/monthly needs…congratulations! But beyond basic needs, how fulfilled are YOU, really? Like on a deep, wildest-dreams-come-true, inner-tiger level? Color in the cherry-pie graph below to show how lit up/stimulated/deeply-and-completely satisfied you are in each category. A fully colored section means it's ringing all your joy and contentment bells, an empty one means it might be time to get a life coach and/or move to Bali for a while.

What does the completed pie tell you? Are you top-loading your financial needs, but neglecting emotional ones? Is your body triathalon ready, but your brain pretty much a useless puddle of nothing? Be brave. Be honest. Don't sugarcoat it. This pie might be a menu for some positive changes.

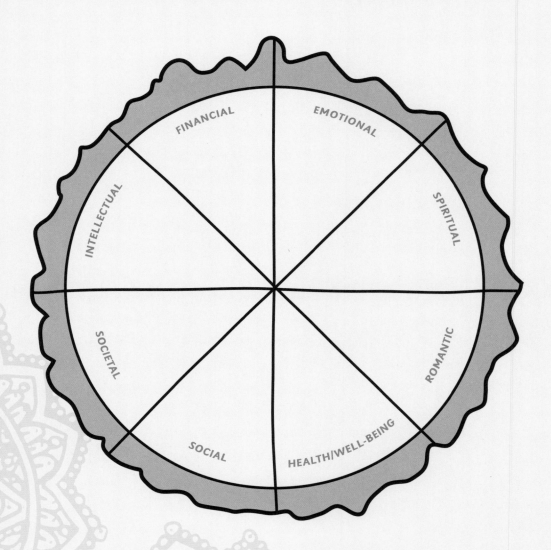

INTELLECTUAL:

You're challenging your mind, trying new things, and learning whenever you can. This can be as small as doing Sudoku/reading blogs—or as big as earning a PhD/solving climate change. The thing you're measuring here is how often you're letting your brain out to play.

FINANCIAL:

You're earning a living that feels secure. You have money for your basic needs, as well as some extra for saving (or spending on kaftans). A surprise bill will only very rarely make you cry.

EMOTIONAL:

You feel seen, heard, and smelled by your family and friends. You don't have any looming grudges that are gnawing at your insides and making you replay conversations hundreds of times in your head. Sadness, frustration, and anxiety might come and go, but they don't stick around long enough to unpack a suitcase.

SPIRITUAL:

You're regularly tickled by the mysteries of life. You might not know what's going on behind the curtain, but you delight in the show. This isn't about religious beliefs—it simply measures your awe-meter. How interested you are in things beyond yourself and your realm of understanding, and how often you get to experience that feeling.

ROMANTIC:

You easily give and receive love/affection/positive attention, and you get to do it frequently. If you're in a relationship, it's one that's healthy and feels totally reciprocated. If you're not, you're feeling good about where you stand. And you can choose to date anytime you want it's totally up to you. Or not. YOU'RE IN CONTROL.

HEALTH/WELL-BEING:

Your basic physical needs are met, and—bonus!—you've also got the time and resources to treat your body with care. Diet, exercise, sleep, and stress management are all a part of this category, which fast food advertisers would love to help you sabotage.

SOCIAL:

You're a part of a community, and you have people you can call on when you need to vent or need company so no one sees you eating brunch alone. You regularly see (or at least talk to) your good friends, who remind you there's life beyond Netflix and pajama pants.

SOCIETAL:

You're doing things that feed your sense of identity. You have a place in the world, and you're actively exploring that place—even if that place doesn't pay you to be there, and even if you're not sure what the next step is from here. The important thing is, you've found something/s you love to do, and you're finding a way to do it/them.

ALTER EGOS

If I could multiply myself and plunk those cool other "dream me's" into the middle of different lives, here's what they'd each be getting up to out there in the world…

ALTERNATIVE ME #1:

Location: _____

Occupation: _____

Description of love/family/home life:

_____

Pet: _____

Hobby: _____

Endearing Nickname:

_____

ALTERNATIVE ME #2:

Location: _____

Occupation: _____

Description of love/family/home life:

_____

Pet: _____

Hobby: _____

Endearing Nickname:

_____

ALTERNATIVE ME #3:

Location: _____

Occupation: _____

Description of love/family/home life:

_____

Pet: _____

Hobby: _____

Endearing Nickname:

_____

Is there anything on this list that you can echo in your current life? For example, if one of your alter egos is a marine biologist, you could go to the beach, volunteer at an aquarium, or try to tame and ride a walrus. Take this opportunity to follow your inner…clues. They might lead you to an uncharted part of your subconscious desire. (Or at the very least, give you a meaningful walrus friendship!)

HONEST ME IS THE BEST POLICY

Got some things you need to get off your chest? Or maybe they're next to your chest, but close enough to your chest that you feel you should move them away from your chest, just to be safe. Either way, see if this helps…

Name of person I'd like to say something to (but haven't, because I don't want the conflict, or I don't feel confident, or one of a million other reasons):

_____

What I'd like to talk about:

_____

_____

_____

The most honest (quite possibly offensive) thing I could say:

_____

_____

_____

The much kinder, more loving, and not-at-all-bridge-burning way to say it:

_____

_____

_____

Name of person I'd like to say something to (but haven't, because I don't want the conflict, or I don't feel confident, or one of a million other reasons):

_____

What I'd like to talk about:

_____

_____

_____

The most honest (quite possibly offensive) thing I could say:

_____

_____

_____

The much kinder, more loving, and not-at-all-bridge-burning way to say it:

_____

_____

_____

Now that you've written it all down on paper…is there a world where you can say these things out loud (the kinder, more loving versions, obvi) and feel better/more honest/more expressive? Your throat chakra has your back (not to mention your voice).

FROM THE TOP O' THE MOUNTAIN

A GUIDED, FILL-IN-THE-BLANK MEDITATION

Imagine you're standing on a mountaintop, overlooking much of the world. When you look down, you

can see _____ , and you can also see all the way
(name of where you live)

to _____ . There is a crowd of people gathered, and they're all
(special place to you personally)

really stoked and joyful. People are hugging, and smiling, and singing _____ .
(song you love)

They're lifting kids on their shoulders and talking about the importance of _____
(thing that's important to you)

and _____ . A hush falls over the crowd when they see you up there.
(another thing that's important to you)

Everyone is excited, anticipatory. With a huge smile, someone calls your name, and a cheer ripples

through the crowd. _____ steps up to you with a smile and puts their hand
(name of an idol of yours)

on your shoulder. You notice that their throat is glowing like a turquoise jewel; in the reflection of

their eyes you see that yours is too. They nod, you nod back. With the same knowing smile, they hand

you a megaphone and say "Thank you. We need this." You take the megaphone, step forward, and

feel the positivity of the crowd as they stop their cheering and look up at you…

Play this scene out in your mind. There are no wrong answers. You can talk to them for as long or short a time as you want. You can use rambling, stream-of-consciousness paragraphs, or one-word statements and long pauses. Whatever you say, they will eat it up. They love you and they're here to listen to you. They will laugh at your jokes, nod at your wisdom, be totally mesmerized by your sincerity. This is your platform, your mountaintop. Let yourself speak.

NOTES-TO-SELF

Don't miss the memo on personal conviction! Fill out these notes, then cut them out and tape them around your house/car/desk/mirror/eyelids—to give yourself some wise-yet-practical reminders of what's important to you, and what you stand for.

PRIORITIZE:
_____
_____
_____
_____
_____

LOVE:
_____
_____
_____
_____
_____

BE:
_____
_____
_____
_____
_____

TAKE TIME TO:
_____
_____
_____
_____
_____

STAY:
_____
_____
_____
_____
_____

YOU ARE:
_____
_____
_____
_____
_____

LIFE IS:
_____
_____
_____
_____
_____

I CONTAIN MULTITUDES

For each section, start by naming a way you define yourself (teacher, lawyer, traveler, cape-wearer, whale-lover, homemade-fanny-pack-advocate). Then fill in the blanks to explore what it's doing for you and your place in the world.

HERE'S HOW IT MIGHT LOOK (EXCEPT NOT REALLY CAUSE ONLY YOU'RE YOU!):

I am a <u>gardener</u>.

This answers my call to <u>nurture living things</u>.

Because it means that I <u>help teeny tiny sprouts become giant, wild tomato plants</u>.

And that makes me feel <u>like some kind of god (even though the plant does most of the work)</u>.

I am a _____ .

This answers my call to _____ .

Because it means that I _____ .

And that makes me feel

_____ .

I am a _____ .

This answers my call to _____ .

Because it means that I _____ .

And that makes me feel

_____ .

I am a _____ .

This answers my call to _____ .

Because it means that I _____ .

And that makes me feel

_____ .

I am a _____ .

This answers my call to _____ .

Because it means that I _____ .

And that makes me feel

_____ .

LOOKING AHEAD . . .

I also hear the call (however quiet, garbled, or

whispery) to _____ .

And I could answer it by doing any or all of these things:

_____

_____

_____

I also hear the call (however quiet, garbled, or

whispery) to _____ .

And I could answer it by doing any or all of these things:

_____

_____

_____

LIVING YOUR BEST LIFE

Are you living a life that's aligned with your true purpose? Do you feel like your career (or artistic pursuit, or random, free-wheeling bohemian lifestyle) is one that makes the most of who you are and the kind of world you want to build? There's no quick 'n' easy answer to a question like this, but your general state of mind might be giving you some clues. Read the statements below, and check all the ones that ring true for you. Where do the majority of your checkmarks fall? If your answer was "in the Nope column," then what can you do to steer things toward more YEPs?

ALIGNED WITH YOUR PURPOSE?

YEP, HECK YEAH!

- [ ] You're so satisfied with the present that you do very little planning about the road ahead. In other words, you already have the meat and potatoes. Anything else would be gravy.

- [ ] Money isn't at the top of your mind (because you'd do what you do for free!).

- [ ] Your energy is most often seated in the heart (love, gratitude).

- [ ] Your life feels expansive; it's open and free, and it's only getting freer and open-er.

- [ ] You create from a place of joy, without much focus on the outcome.

- [ ] It almost feels like you're being selfish. Are you the kid who robbed the candy store?

UH, NOPE.

- [ ] What you'll do, how to do it, how to get there, and a million other what/who/how/when's that you have no control over (sorcerers excepted).

- [ ] You count every penny you make during this painstaking chapter that robs you of your valuable time.

- [ ] Your energy loves being in the head (fear, analysis, control).

- [ ] Your life feels constrictive (no small, enclosed spaces needed).

- [ ] Screw the process, the product is all that matters.

- [ ] You're frequently resentful of kids and candy stores.

YEP TOTAL = _____

NOPE TOTAL = _____

USE YOUR VOICE FOR GOOD

How often do you say things about people when they're not around? How often are you the person other people are saying things to about other other people when they're not around?

DAY 1:
Spend a day clocking what comes out of your mouth about people you know (or don't know), and make notes about what you've dished. Any specific observations? General ones? What's the word on your words? Mostly good, mostly bad, or a whole lotta in between?

_____

_____

_____

DAY 2:
Alrighty. Now be the person who only says nice things about people who aren't there. You don't have to be inauthentic. Meaning, if someone comes up in conversation and you truly can't think of a single nice thing to say about them, you don't have to. But don't participate in saying anything negative. And if you can, challenge yourself to say something, anything that rings as a compliment.

INSTEAD OF:
"He's such an insane micro-manager. He thinks there's a better way to do literally everything."

TRY SOMETHING LIKE:
"I'll give him this. He's passionate about his job."

OR THIS:
"He's definitely teaching me how to be more patient. And I'll be grateful when I graduate from patience-college."

There shouldn't be many cases where you can't think of anything nice. (And if there are, then maybe reevaluate your social circles!?) In most cases, you'll just be choosing to add something kind that you maybe wouldn't have said otherwise. And isn't that the sort of homework you'd want someone else to do about you?

NOW FOR SOME BACK-PATTING!

Not-nice things you wanted to (but didn't) say:

_____

_____

_____

The very nice things you said instead:

_____

_____

_____

MY IDEAL WORLD

If I could wave a giant wand over the world, and have all of my druthers*…my abracadabra would create a utopian life that looked like this (feel free to write out what your perfect dream existence is— or just do little bullet lists or even doodle it if you prefer!):

ON A GLOBAL SCALE:

_____

_____

IN MY PERSONAL LIFE/
MY OWN BEHAVIOR:

_____

_____

ON A NATIONAL SCALE:

_____

_____

IN MY INNER SELF/
INNER LIFE:

_____

_____

IN MY HOUSEHOLD:

_____

_____

IN MY CITY:

_____

_____

IN MY NEIGHBORHOOD:

_____

_____

*and cake**
**and eat it, too

THIRD EYE

The next leap in consciousness comes from our third eye chakra, which transports us beyond duality ("me"/"you") and into the awareness of a much-less-taxing superconsciousness ("all that is"). The third eye has a vision that allows us to pierce life's confusing veils (you know, the whole time-is-a-construct and money-isn't-real song and dance), and gives us the power of (at minimum) a strong intuition and (at maximum) transcendent mystical revelation. It is the chakra of imagination, insight, and psychic abilities—and yes, we all have access to it, even if we grew up in small, closed-minded towns.

WHEN YOUR THIRD EYE'S RIGHT:
You'll be in tune with subtle energies, whether you're aware of it or not. You'll see life clearly and make decisions easily, with no emotional attachment to outcome (and no coin flips needed!). You might even have a healthy, reciprocal relationship with your subconscious…

"I wasn't sure which job to take, but I had a dream about a grateful wolf, so I'm saying yes to the dog shelter."

WHEN YOUR THIRD EYE'S BLOCKED:
You might notice a dull memory and poor dream recall. Mistrustful of your inner voice, you can become overwhelmed by details (rather than staying the course on the big picture you used to know and love). Logic and cynicism win over depth and magic…and somewhere, possibly, an angel loses its wings.

"I don't know where to go for brunch. Give me three hours to read all the Yelp reviews."

WHEN YOUR THIRD EYE'S OVERACTIVE:
You'll have difficulty concentrating, or even feeling grounded in reality. Lost in fantasies, plagued by nightmares, and prone to paranoia and mood disorders—gah!—might wanna solve this one sooner rather than later. In some cases, an overactive third eye can even induce hallucinations.

"You'd tell me if I was a malevolent assassin that's been programmed by the government, right?"

KEY CONCEPTS:
* Intuition
* Psychic Perception
* Dreams
* Imagination
* Foresight
* Vision
* Manifestation
* Awareness

LOCATION:
Between the Eyebrows

TO OPEN AND BALANCE YOUR THIRD EYE:
Color: Indigo or Purple
Essential Oils: Basil, Frankincense
Stones:
* Overactive = Emerald/Sapphire
* Blocked = Diamond/Herkimer Diamond
* For General Balance = Lapis Lazuli

Yoga Pose: Downward Dog
Musical Key: A
Food: Eggplant, Purple Cabbage, Purple Kale

**THIRD EYE PLAYLIST
(SONGS IN THE KEY OF A):**

"September" (Earth, Wind & Fire)
"Dancing Queen" (ABBA)
"Sweet Emotion" (Aerosmith)
"Hold the Line" (Toto)
"Take Me Home Country Roads" (John Denver)
"Giving You the Best That I've Got" (Anita Baker)
"Buffalo Soldier" (Bob Marley)
"Mrs. Robinson" (Paul Simon)
"Just Like Heaven" (The Cure)

DEAR ME, PART 2

Transport yourself to the future for a few minutes…"the" future meaning the one where you're eighty years old, happy, healthy, fulfilled, etc. Write a letter to yourself as you are now. Tell yourself what you have to look forward to. Remind yourself what's important. Ask yourself to get into that crocheting workshop or start doing tai chi in the park at 6am now, so you can get a leg up on your progress.

JUMPING OUTSIDE THE BOX

Just as the third eye coaxes us to move beyond duality ("me vs. you," "us vs. them," "real dessert vs. cheese plate"), we can coax ourselves to melt limiting boundaries and help stoke our third eye consciousness.

Yank yourself out of your deeply-defined habitual ruts with the following recipes for personal expansion. See how many challenges you can complete!

WATCH A FLICK FROM EACH OF THESE (NOT SUPER MAINSTREAM) GENRES:

☐ Bollywood Horror

☐ Ostern

☐ Killer Car

READ ONE OR MORE OF THESE POSSIBLY-NOT-ON-YOUR-SHELF BOOKS:

☐ A coming-of-age tale set in a foreign country

☐ A collection of poems or essays about nature

☐ A hybrid genre (e.g., sci-fi/mystery, historical/romance, zombie/noir)

COOK AN UNEXPECTED DISH WITH:

☐ Saffron

☐ Kohlrabi

☐ Dragonfruit

HEY, TRY THIS!

Your breath is an immediate link to the infinite present moment, and nothing will make you feel more infinite than a good 2.2 seconds of conscious awareness.

So for the rest of the day, whenever you remember to (and that's literally whenever you remember to), take three conscious breaths. You can do this wherever you are, and in the middle of whatever you're doing. Feeding the fish? Three conscious breaths. Trying on a skort? Three conscious breaths. Picking up the foreign diplomats and taking them to In-N-Out? Three conscious breaths.

That's meditation, animal-style. Fries are extra.

AFFIRMATIONS

To be spoken aloud, or silently projected (as good practice for using your psychic voice). There's no wrong way to use affirmations—you can say them anywhere from one to 37 million times per day (but two or three usually does the trick). Say 'em, own 'em, and feel the wisdom your third eye has known all along.

LIFE IS A DREAM, AND I CHOOSE TO BE A LUCID DREAMER. IT'S FUN TO CREATE THE LIFE AND STORY THAT I WANT...AND MAYBE AT SOME POINT I'LL GET TO FLY OR TURN INTO A TIGER OR SOMETHING.

I AM IN TUNE WITH MY HIGHEST SELF, AND I CONNECT WITH THE WISDOM OF THE UNIVERSE. THE WISDOM IS ALWAYS THERE, I JUST NEED TO LISTEN. AND THEN BELIEVE. AND THEN WRITE IT DOWN BECAUSE IT'S REALLY FRUSTRATING TO FORGET EPIPHANIES.

I HEAR MY INTUITION LOUDLY AND CLEARLY, AND I KNOW THAT IT'S RIGHT. IT'S ALWAYS RIGHT. IN FACT, I'LL DO WHAT IT'S TELLING ME JUST SO IT WILL SHUT UP ABOUT IT FOR A SECOND AND STOP GLOATING.

READING THE SIGNS

Have you ever had a week where the same word, phrase, or image keeps showing up again and again? A butterfly lands on your arm, then someone walks by wearing a butterfly T-shirt, and THEN your waiter asks if you'd like to try that night's special: a steak, which is cut butterfly style.

It could be that you're in tune with signs and messages from your subtle energy body. In a vast world, full of trillions of things that aren't butterflies, your attention is subconsciously drawn towards the few things that are butterflies, because the metaphor of transformation is something that resonates with you right now.

Start paying attention to repeated signs and symbols. Note them here when they happen, and see if you can make sense out of them. They might be omens guiding your way.

SOMETHING I KEEP SEEING/HEARING:
_____

WHAT IT MIGHT BE TELLING ME:
_____
_____
_____
_____
_____

SOMETHING I KEEP SEEING/HEARING:
_____

WHAT IT MIGHT BE TELLING ME:
_____
_____
_____
_____
_____

SOMETHING I KEEP SEEING/HEARING:
_____

WHAT IT MIGHT BE TELLING ME:
_____
_____
_____
_____

DREAM JOURNAL

For the next few nights, keep a dream journal. Keep a pen and notebook by your bedside, and as soon as you wake up (even if it's for a middle-of-the-night toilet adventure), jot down a few notes or key words about the dream you just had. In the morning, flesh the notes out into a paragraph or two. Circle any emotional words, and note them here, along with the people/places/activities/objects those emotions were associated with. Now play dream wizard. What do you suppose those people/objects/ etc. were symbolizing? What advice can you take away from this seemingly nonsensical dream?

HERE'S HOW AN ENTRY MIGHT LOOK:

Emotion: Frustration

Associated Elements:
* A late train, which might symbolize feeling stuck and not getting anywhere
* A broken phone, which might symbolize a communication breakdown
* A person blocking my way and not letting me pass, which might symbolize feeling unheard? Unimportant? (And feeling stuck again!)

The Takeaway: I'm feeling stuck right now, and like I'm not in control of my own progress. I want to express myself, but deep down I feel that either I won't be listened to, or that it's going to be impossible to get through to the other person. (Or maybe my subconscious just wants a new phone?)

Emotion:

_____

Associated Elements:

_____ , which might symbolize
_____ .

_____ , which might symbolize
_____ .

_____ , which might symbolize
_____ .

The Takeaway: _____

_____

_____ .

Emotion:

_____

Associated Elements:

_____ , which might symbolize
_____ .

_____ , which might symbolize
_____ .

_____ , which might symbolize
_____ .

The Takeaway: _____

_____

_____ .

KNOCKING DOWN WALLS
(OR USING LOTS OF LADDERS)

Ever hear a not-so-nice whisper in the back of your mind when you go to do something that's not in your normal routine? "You're not really gonna try and sing are you? Even your speaking voice is annoying…" The truth is, we all hear those whispers, and we all hear them because someone along the way made us feel tinier, duller, and much less amazing than we really are. Your third eye is here to help you see those limiting beliefs for what they are, so that you can see right past them. Hopefully that'll give you something to sing about.

SOME LIMITING BELIEFS I'VE GOT ABOUT MYSELF:

I can't _____ .

I'm not good at _____ .

I was never meant to _____ .

I won't ever have _____ .

I'll never be up for _____ .

WHERE DID THESE BELIEFS COME FROM? OOOH, LET'S NAME NAMES! THESE ARE THE NAYSAYERS, THE NON-BELIEVERS, THE NEGATIVE-SEED PLANTERS FROM MY PAST:

_____

_____

_____

_____

_____

NOW, FLIP THE SCRIPT*:

I could _____ .

I can learn to be good at _____ .

I might be meant to _____ .

I will one day have _____ .

I'm totally up for _____ .

*Write the exact same things in these blanks. Which is something you DEFINITELY CAN do.

FIELD TRIP!

What's the best way to widen your perspective on the world (besides updating your lens prescription)? Spend a day in someone else's shoes ... exploring a neighborhood you've never been to, attending an event you've never heard of, or wandering around a cosplay convention, where you feel out of place because you didn't come dressed in something made of foam core. Fill out these permission slips for a few deep dives into different cultural (or sub-cultural) planets ... then take yourself on a field trip sometime in the not-too-distant future! Your level of participation is totally up to what you're feeling that day. When you return to your home planet, jot down anything you noticed/loved about your foray. Hopefully you'll expand your understanding of the world, and (depending on how handy you are with foam core) you might even pick up a new passion.

Today's date: _____

_____ has my permission to attend (location or event) as an instant reminder of the vastness of the world, complexity of individuals, and boring-ness of personal boxes.

Signature: _____

Date field trip taken: _____

Observations, lessons, thoughtful musings:

_____

_____

_____

_____

Today's date: _____

_____ has my permission to attend (location or event) as an instant reminder of the vastness of the world, complexity of individuals, and boring-ness of personal boxes.

Signature: _____

Date field trip taken: _____

Observations, lessons, thoughtful musings:

_____

_____

_____

_____

Today's date: _____

_____ has my permission to attend (location or event) as an instant reminder of the vastness of the world, complexity of individuals, and boring-ness of personal boxes.

Signature: _____

Date field trip taken: _____

Observations, lessons, thoughtful musings:

_____

_____

_____

_____

CAN YOU FEEL IT?

Visualization is a wonderful tool for manifesting what you want—but so is its less-talked-about younger sibling: emotion. Fill the space below with stuff (or experiences or relationships or events or perfect haircuts) you'd like to see unfold in your universe. You can do it in pictures or in words, depending on whether you're allergic to vision boards or prefer to show vs. tell it. Then pair what you're manifesting with the emotional quality it carries. "When I've built my own treehouse, I'll feel so proud of the crazy accomplishment I've pulled off." That emotion is what you should hang on to while you're visualizing. Because while visualizing is a great vehicle for manifesting, emotion is the (totally free and clean) gas that makes it go!

SOME OF THE THINGS, JOBS, ADVENTURES I SEE MYSELF HAVING/DOING/GOING ON:

1. _____

2. _____

3. _____

When I imagine my future self having already gotten a hold of _____ , I know that future
                                                                (insert thing #1)
self feels _____ . So the key to calling _____ into my life is to visualize
          (emotion)   (insert thing #1)
it while also stoking a feeling of_____ .
                                 (see emotion above)

When I imagine my future self having already gotten a hold of _____ , I know that future
                                                                (insert thing #2)
self feels _____ . So the key to calling _____ into my life is to visualize
          (emotion)   (insert thing #2)
it while also stoking a feeling of_____ .
                                 (see emotion above)

When I imagine my future self having already gotten a hold of _____ , I know that future
                                                                (insert thing #3)
self feels _____ . So the key to calling _____ into my life is to visualize
          (emotion)   (insert thing #3)
it while also stoking a feeling of_____ .
                                 (see emotion above)

EYE OPENING

One technique for opening the third eye is closing your (regular) eyes, and visualizing the infinity symbol between your eyebrows. Visualize it burning with indigo light while you breathe deeply.

Once you have it firmly in your (closed-eye) sight, incant the sound "Om" for the entire length of each exhalation. See how long you can extend it. See how far into inner space you can see. Anything cool in there, like limitless peace or expansive personal potential? Asking for a friend.

FLY WITH OWL

According to shamanic wisdom keepers, owls symbolize the journey between worlds—an ability to fly beyond the earthly plane and return with the knowledge of astral dimensions. To know the owl is to know the part of yourself that is connected to your guides, teachers, and ancestors. No wonder she/he/they are so wise! Feel free to color in the owl (if you're feeling it).

DREAM DATE

One way to connect with your astral guides and teachers is in the dream plane—either while sleeping or while in meditation. Use this page to declare your intentions to meet your guides. Make your declaration before you lay down to sleep and see if they introduce themselves in your dreams. Sleeping with amethyst, clear quartz, or lapis lazuli under your pillow will amplify the connection. Remember that your guides love communicating; if it doesn't work the first time, try again!

TO WHOM IT MAY CONCERN (AKA MY GUIDES AND TEACHERS):

I, _____ desire to have an open connection with you, and would
    (name)
love to meet you almost-in-person, in my dreams (or wherever is convenient).
Please meet me if you're free tonight…I will be there with open arms! Otherwise,
let's try for tomorrow?

If you want celestial bonus points, you can also write your own intentions in a whole
lot more detail below. Either way, your third eye's got you.

_____

_____

_____

_____

_____

_____

_____

_____

CROWN

The last of the major chakras is the crown. Located at the top of the head and open like a funnel to mainline divine energy straight into your system, it's the Grand Central Station of cosmic consciousness. The crown chakra links us to universal awareness—the knowledge that all energy is one, and we are but a breath of air in the great sky of life (or skies of life, depending on whether you subscribe to a multiverse theory or not). This is the chakra of enlightenment. Of highest being. Of paradox, because the more we talk about what it is, the further away from it we're getting. Y'know?

WHEN YOUR CROWN'S RIGHT:
TBH, a fully open and flowing crown chakra is a rare find, but you can certainly foster a healthy crown that puts you somewhere between spiritual impotence and total enlightenment. Some good signs that your crown is open: you feel a connection to something beyond yourself and the physical world, you feel totally confident and secure (but not in an arrogant, ego-driven way), and you put your energy toward the greater good of all beings—even when no one is looking.

"Of course my ex and I are starting a charity together. We've always gotten along, and the endangered turtles need us."

WHEN YOUR CROWN'S BLOCKED:
Disconnection becomes the mayor of your life. You may feel isolated, lonely, and hopeless. Life lacks meaning, though you're not sure why, and fixing it seems hopeless because you're too darn lethargic to take care of yourself, let alone the entirety of your reality.

"I don't get it. Why do people smile?"

WHEN YOUR CROWN'S OVERACTIVE:
Ego, greed, and materialism are your shiniest qualities. Your lack of empathy might tip all the way to outright aggression, and the mere mention of spirituality will make your skeptical mind cringe until it forms a row of icicles. Keep an eye out for visits from ghosts of various Christmases.

"Will you shut up about your stupid piano recital? I'm trying to count my millions!"

KEY CONCEPTS:
* Enlightenment
* Consciousness
* Divine Connection
* Transcendence
* Oneness

LOCATION:
Top of the Head, Floating Just Above It

TO OPEN AND BALANCE YOUR CROWN:
Color: Violet (or White)
Essential Oils: Lotus, Water Lily, Sage, Juniper, Lavender
Stones:
* Overactive = Charoite / Sugulite
* Blocked = Celestite
* For General Balance = Amethyst / Clear Quartz

Yoga Pose: Shoulder Stand
Musical Key: B
Food: N/A (Detox and fasting are more helpful for this spiritually-calibrated chakra than physical, anatomy-focused foods, but a clean diet never hurt anybody. Definitely ease off the toxins and drink more water than you think you should.)

CROWN PLAYLIST (SONGS IN THE KEY OF B):

"Sweet Caroline" (Neil Diamond)
"You Are the Sunshine of My Life" (Stevie Wonder)
"The Boxer" (Simon & Garfunkel)
"Love Will Keep Us Together" (Captain & Tennille)
"Revolution" (The Beatles)
"Adagio in B Major" (Mozart)
"She Cries Your Name" (Beth Orton)
"Burning Down the House" (Talking Heads)

LETTING GO & CALLING IN

When's the last time you gave your life a bit of spring cleaning? Take this chance to take a broom to the cobwebs of old vibes and behaviors that no longer serve you, then declare what you'd like to call in to freshen things up. A new ottoman might be nice ...

**THINGS THAT NO LONGER SERVE ME,
THAT I'M POLITELY SHOWING THE DOOR:**

ACTIVITIES

ENERGY

ATTITUDES

THINGS I'M MAKING ROOM FOR, IN THE HOPES
THEY'LL STICK AROUND FOR A WHILE:

EVENTS

EMOTIONS

ENERGY

CONTEMPLATION

For these eyes-open meditations, simply be present and breathe deeply while staring at these oft-taken-for-granted miracles…

A FLOWER

A CANDLE FLAME

WATER (ANY WATER. EVEN A PUDDLE)

THE MOON (OR REALLY— ANY MOON. THANK YOU, INTERNET!)

BE THE CHANGE

The crown is a funnel that's poised and ready to unload all kinds of warm and loving goodness into you from the top down. Groove with the goodness, and you'll find you don't want to keep it to yourself. What about brainstorming some ways to share the love with the planet you're riding around on?

POSITIVE CHANGES THAT WOULD POSITIVELY IMPACT THE PLANET IN A POSITIVE WAY:

Teeny tiny:
_____
_____

Regular tiny:
_____
_____

Small:
_____
_____

Medium:
_____
_____

Medium plus:
_____
_____

Large minus:
_____
_____

Large:
_____
_____

Gigantic:
_____
_____

Monstrous:
_____
_____

Inconceivably absurd:
_____
_____

SMILES FOR MILES

Try this simple exercise and see how much sunshine you can spread in your inner and outer world. Kind of like magic, isn't it?

Sit and smile for one minute. (That's right. A nice, by yourself, smile-at-nothing kinda smile.)

Now relax your mouth, but keep the feeling of smiling. (Yes, exactly like "smizing.")

NOW YOU'RE GOING TO SEND THAT SMILEY FEELING TO DIFFERENT PARTS OF YOUR BODY:

Smile with the top of your head.

Smile with your heart.

Smile with your fingertips.

With the base of your spine.

With your spleen (wherever that is!).

And now— with your whole being.

ONLY STOP IF/WHEN YOU WANT TO!
(OTHERWISE, LET'S KEEP THIS PARTY GOING FOREVER.)

HUSH PLEASE

Can you put a lid on your brain noise and give your soul thirty minutes of silence per day?

Shut down the stress, the busyness, the mental chatter, and let yourself be. You don't need to meditate—just take the input away and see what happens. You might find you enjoy having half an hour that's free of opinions, commercials, and political rants. Imagine that.

THAT MEANS:

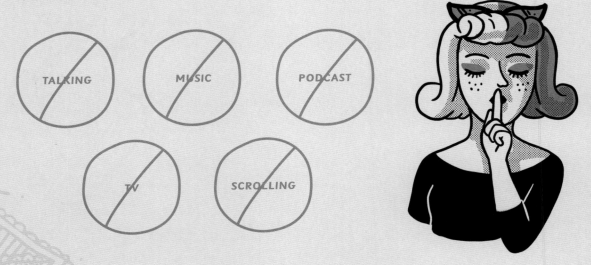

TALKING

MUSIC

PODCAST

TV

SCROLLING

CROWN MANTRA

"So Hum," which translates to "I am that I am," is a fantastic mantra for meditating. On each inhalation, say (or think!) the syllable "So." On each exhalation, "Hum."

SO HUM.

SO HUM.

SO HUM.

I AM THAT I AM.

(Definitely not to be confused with Ho Hum, which is a useful mantra for expressing boredom. Or So Dumb, which is the mantra of puns like these.)

LANGUAGE UPGRADE

You may be using language that limits your possibilities, and you might not even be aware of it. Are you prone to firing off sentences that start with "I can't," "I want," and "I have to"? Think of these like instructions that you're giving the universe. The universe, being a realm of highest consciousness, capable of manifesting anything in an instant—is a very literal domain. Not a lot of room for context and nuance there, and certainly no understanding of sarcasm or modern colloquialisms.

In the realm of manifestation, "I can't," "I want," and "I have to" are instructions that tell your energy patterns that you wish to be incapable, impoverished, and subservient…Probably not the wish list you were going for.

> **BUMMER STATEMENT**
> "I can't go to the movies tonight."
>
> **POSITIVE TRANSLATION**
> "I can enjoy a night in tonight."

FILL IN THE NEGATIVE BLANKS BELOW THEN UPGRADE YOUR LANGUAGE IN A POSITIVE WAY THAT DECLARES YOU TO BE CAPABLE, WEALTHY, AND THE MASTER OF YOUR DESTINY.

I can't _____ .

I can _____ .

I shouldn't _____ .

I should _____ .

I have to _____ .

I get to _____ .

I need _____ .

I desire _____ .

I don't want _____ .

I want _____ .

I don't _____ .

I do _____ .

I hate _____ .

I love _____ .

DAILY INTENTIONS

For the next week, at the start of each day, write an intentional statement that includes two or three emotional adjectives.

Before bed, reflect on your experiences—big and small—and write down anything that happened that sparked those feelings. Did you catch a glimpse of support when someone held the door for you? Did you feel a tiny glimmer of gratitude when you pulled up to a red carpet parking space just as someone else was pulling out?

Use the same intentions for two or three days in a row, and see what happens. (Hint: the more you notice them, the more they will show up for you. Intentions are attention hogs.)

"TODAY, I INTEND TO FEEL CHALLENGED, SMART, AND USEFUL."

"TODAY, I INTEND TO FEEL LOVED AND SUPPORTED."

DAILY INTENTION:

_____

HOW/WHERE IT SHOWED UP FOR ME:

_____
_____
_____
_____

DAILY INTENTION:

_____

HOW/WHERE IT SHOWED UP FOR ME:

_____
_____
_____
_____

DAILY INTENTION:

_____

HOW/WHERE IT SHOWED UP FOR ME:

_____
_____
_____
_____

DAILY INTENTION:

_____

HOW/WHERE IT SHOWED UP FOR ME:

_____
_____
_____
_____

DAILY INTENTION:

_____

HOW/WHERE IT SHOWED UP FOR ME:

_____
_____
_____
_____

DAILY INTENTION:

_____

HOW/WHERE IT SHOWED UP FOR ME:

_____
_____
_____
_____

CLEAN-EATING STAR CHART

Fasting is excellent for the crown, but we all gotta eat! So when it comes to "feeding" your crown, think whole, think clean, think green. Vegetables like spinach, carrots, broccoli, sweet potatoes, beets, asparagus, and kale offer tons of vitamins and minerals—with lots of fiber to boot! Low-glycemic fruits like berries and oranges will satisfy your sweet tooth without loading your body with sugar. Organic bone broth is a great way to heal your gut and recharge your immune system. And herbs/spices like garlic, turmeric, ginger, and cinnamon are natural ways to fight infection and inflammation. A good guideline is to "eat the rainbow," which means eating as many different colored foods in one day as you can. That ensures that you're getting a well-rounded roster of nutrients in your system. You want the whole team working for you, rather than just a couple of players.

So how about devoting the next seven days to nourishing your crown through your stomach? Just go one day (or one bite) at a time if you have to. At the end of each day, mark off your daily accomplishment with a big ol' gold star—because every self-respecting grownup deserves kid-like credit for doing something hard.

	SUN	MON	TUES	WED	THU	FRI	SAT
NO ALCOHOL							
NO CAFFEINE							
NO SUGAR							
NO DAIRY							
NO GRAINS							
NO PROCESSED OR FROZEN FOODS							
ALL ORGANIC INGREDIENTS							

CROWNED WITH MY BEST SELF

When I am at my best, I _____ , _____ , and
_____ . I know that I have the potential to _____
_____ , so that's what I will do. (Starting _____ .)
Rather than express negativity, _____ , _____ , or
_____ , my goal each day will be to express _____ ,
_____ , _____ , and _____ .
Hopefully, I will help others around me feel _____ and _____
instead of _____ and _____ . And that's pretty great, because
hopefully that will (maybe a tiny bit selfishly) make me feel _____ , which will make
me want to _____ , which will (unselfishly) create more _____ .
What's the opposite of a vicious circle? A virtuous triangle? If I want to be a shining example for
others, I can always choose to _____ , _____ , or
_____ . And if I want to be the all-out, balls-to-the-wall shiniest, then I can
turn it up a notch and _____ . In the
interest of treating myself more kindly, I can easily _____
and _____ . In fact, I've already treated myself kindly by
_____ and _____ .*

*Yes, stars are deserved and completely appropriate. You may draw or affix them here:

OM SWEET OM...